THE INEQUALITY OF MAN

By the same Author

    DAEDALUS
    CALLINICUS
    ANIMAL BIOLOGY; with J. S. Huxley
    POSSIBLE WORLDS and Other Essays
    ENZYMES
    THE CAUSES OF EVOLUTION

By his Wife

    MAN'S WORLD
    MOTHERHOOD AND ITS ENEMIES
    BROTHER TO BERT
    I BRING NOT PEACE

THE
INEQUALITY OF MAN
AND OTHER ESSAYS

By

J. B. S. HALDANE, F.R.S.

SIR WILLIAM DUNN READER IN BIOCHEMISTRY
IN THE UNIVERSITY OF CAMBRIDGE:
HEAD OF GENETICAL DEPARTMENT
JOHN INNES HORTICULTURAL INSTITUTION, MERTON
SOMETIME FELLOW OF NEW COLLEGE
OXFORD

LONDON

CHATTO & WINDUS

1932

PRINTED IN GREAT BRITAIN BY
R. & R. CLARK, LTD., EDINBURGH

PREFACE

THIS book contains a rather mixed bag of writings. They were written for several different audiences, varying from the readers of the daily Press to the members of the Royal Institution. They include two reviews of the writings of other popularizers of science, namely, Bertrand Russell and Sir James Jeans. Six of them, namely, 'The Place of Science in Western Civilization', 'My Philosophy of Life' (a broadcast address), 'What I think about', 'Birth Control', 'The Story of my Health', and 'If Jesus lived To-day' were originally parts of series to which I was a contributor. And 'The Gold-Makers' is a story, which I take this opportunity of publishing, since it is rather unlikely that I shall ever write enough fiction to fill a volume.

So I hope to please a variety of tastes. The serious-minded reader may begin at 'The Origin of Life', or 'Prehistory in the Light of Genetics'. The less solemn may well start on 'The Gold-Makers' or 'The Story of my Health', a topic which, unlike the other contributors to the series, I treated with levity.

But in spite of this heterogeneity a single idea runs through the book. How does science affect human life? We are living in a time of crisis brought on by the refusal of our rulers to adjust our economic organization to the vast increase of productive power brought about by science. As readers of 'The Gold-Makers' will discover, my views on economics are neither original nor

profound. But I have some claim to write on human
biology, and about half the essays deal with this topic.

The majority of the contents have already appeared
in one of the following periodicals: The *Rationalist
Annual*, *Harper's Magazine*, the *Century Magazine*, the
Proceedings of the Royal Institution, the *Spectator*, the
Daily Express, the *Daily Herald*, the *Daily Chronicle*,
the *St. Louis Post-Dispatch*, the *Passing Show*, the
Literary Guide, the *Listener*, the *Realist*, the *Strand
Magazine*, *Nash's Magazine*, the *Saturday Evening Post*,
the *Cosmopolitan Magazine*, and the *Week-End Review*.
I must particularly thank Messrs. Watts & Co. and
Messrs. Allen, Unwin & Co. for permission to reprint
the essays which have already appeared in book form.

It is likely that the views which I have expressed in
these essays do not form a wholly coherent logical
system. This is natural for two reasons. I have been
far too busy with my main occupations of research and
teaching to evolve a complete philosophy of life. And if
my opinions had not changed in the course of the five
years during which this book was written, I should be
ready for the grave.

To remove a misconception which has frequently
found its way into print, I take this opportunity of
declaring my non-identity with my father, Professor
J. S. Haldane. It is true that our opinions differ mainly
on questions of emphasis and terminology rather than
of fact. But they are sufficiently different to have
allowed an ingenious American writer to convict us, in
our joint capacity, of flagrant inconsistency. I hope that
in future my intellectual sins will not be visited on him.

Finally, I wish to disclaim about half the statements
which have recently been attributed to me by various

journals. One completely imaginary interview with me has been published. Others have been perfectly genuine. But some have been of intermediate accuracy. Something like the following dialogue has taken place:

Q. What is the moon made of?

A. I don't know. From its density and from what we conjecture about its origin, its surface probably consists of silicates.

Q. What are silicates?

A. Most rocks except chalk, limestone, and sandstone are silicates. So is glass.

Q. Is the moon's surface solid?

A. Well, there are some pretty big cracks in it.

This apparently harmless statement is liable to become: 'Moon made of broken glass. Eminent scientist's startling theory.' The theories which I propound in this book may or may not be startling, but they are at least my own.

J. B. S. HALDANE.

July 1932.

TABLE OF CONTENTS

THE SCIENTIFIC POINT OF VIEW

SCIENCE affects the average man and woman in two ways already. He or she benefits by its applications, driving in a motor-car or omnibus instead of a horse-drawn vehicle, being treated for disease by a doctor or surgeon rather than a priest or a witch, and being killed with an automatic pistol or a shell in place of a dagger or a battle-axe. It also affects his or her opinions. Almost everyone believes that the earth is round, and the heavens nearly empty, instead of solid. And we are beginning to believe in our animal ancestry and the possibility of vast improvements in human nature by biological methods.

But science can do something far bigger for the human mind than the substitution of one set of beliefs for another, or the inculcation of scepticism regarding accepted opinions. It can gradually spread among humanity as a whole the point of view that prevails among research workers, and has enabled a few thousand men and a few dozen women to create the science on which modern civilization rests. For if we are to control our own and one another's actions as we are learning to control nature, the scientific point of view must come out of the laboratory and be applied to the events of daily life. It is foolish to think that the outlook which has already revolutionized industry, agriculture, war, and medicine will prove useless when applied to the family, the nation, or the human race.

Unfortunately, the growing realization of this fact is

opening the door to innumerable false prophets who
are advertising their own pet theories in sociology as
scientific. Science is continually telling us through their
mouths that we are doomed unless we give up smoking,
adopt—or abolish—birth control, and so forth. Now it
is not my object to support any scientific theory, but
merely the scientific standpoint. What are the characteristics of that standpoint? In the first place, it
attempts to be truthful and, therefore, impartial. And
it carries impartiality a great deal further than does the
legal point of view. A good judge will try to be impartial between Mr. John Smith and Mr. Chang Sing.
A good scientist will be impartial between Mr. Smith,
a tape-worm, and the solar system. He will leave behind
him his natural repulsion of the tape-worm, which
would lead him to throw it away instead of studying it
as carefully as a statue or a symphony, and his awe for
the solar system, which led his predecessors either to
worship its constituents, or at least to regard them as
inscrutable servants of the Almighty, too exalted for
human comprehension.

Such an attitude leads the scientist to a curious
mixture of pride and humility. The solar system turns
out to be a group of bodies rather small in comparison
with many of their neighbours, and executing their
movements according to simple and easily intelligible
laws. But he himself is a rather aberrant member of the
same order as the monkeys, while his mind is at the
mercy of a number of chemical processes in his body
which he can understand but little and control hardly
at all.

In so far as it places all phenomena on the same
emotional level, the scientific point of view may be

called the God's-eye view. But it differs profoundly from that which religions have attributed to the Almighty in being ethically neutral. Science cannot determine what is right and wrong, and should not try to. It can work out the consequences of various actions, but it cannot pass judgment on them. The bacteriologist can merely point out that pollution of the public water supply is likely to cause as many deaths as letting off a bomb in the public street. But he is no better equipped than anyone else in possession of the knowledge he has gained, for determining whether these two acts are equally wrong. The enemies of science alternately abuse its exponents for being deaf to moral considerations and for interfering in ethical problems which do not concern them. Both of these criticisms cannot be right.

Now the tendency of the average man has always been to dwell on the emotional and ethical side of a case rather than on facts of the somewhat dull kind which interest the scientist. Let me take two examples, the problem of the American negro and the problem of disease. A large number of Americans hold that the negro is definitely inferior to the white man, and should, as far as possible, be segregated from him. Others believe that he should enjoy the same rights. The biologist cannot decide between them. He can point out that the negro's skull is more ape-like than the white's, but his hairless skin less so, and so forth. But he can note the results of the two divergent political views as to the negro. In the country districts of the Southern States the birth-rate of the negro population exceeds the death-rate. In the southern towns, and all through the north, more negroes die than are born. Their high death-rates are due to the fact that, in an environment suitable to a white man, they die of consumption and other diseases, just as the white man dies on the West Coast of Africa, the negro's original home.

So if you keep the negro out of cars, factories, and so forth, or frighten him away from contact with whites by an occasional lynching, you drive him back to the cotton fields where he lives healthily and breeds rapidly, thus creating a negro problem for future generations. But if you extend the hand of fellowship to him you also infect him with your maladies, besides establishing in your midst a reservoir of disease germs.

These results are quite typical of those obtained when our action is guided either by raw emotion or political dogma rather than scientific thought. The main bio-logical effect of the American Civil War was to raise the negroes' death-rate and lower their birth-rate so enor-mously that it was only between 1910 and 1920 that the number of negroes in the United States increased as much as it had done in the decade before the Civil War. The number of negroes thus killed was far greater than the casualty list of the Civil War. If to-morrow the coloured population of the Southern States, but not the white, were given free access to cheap whisky and methods of birth control, the number of negroes would probably begin to fall off! I believe that there are many other political questions, both national and inter-national, whose sting would be removed by a similar consideration of biological facts.

Our approach to the problem of disease is even less rational. I am not thinking of Christian scientists or spiritual healers, but of the average man or woman who has a certain belief in the results of modern medicine, and even of a part of the medical profession itself.

Serious illness in ourselves or our friends always rouses a good deal of emotion. Now, when we are emotional about a subject we feel a need to believe something about it, and we do not care very much whether our beliefs are rational. The pre-Christian attitude to disease was that it was a punishment from some deity for a sin either of the sick person, his family, or the whole community. Jesus did not take this view. When asked concerning a man born blind, 'Who did sin, this man, or his parents, that he was born blind? . . .' he replied, 'Neither hath this man sinned, nor his parents, but that the works of God should be made manifest in him'. This is not so unlike the attitude of the scientist who regards a case of disease as a manifestation of a natural law, which can only be cured or prevented when research has revealed the working of the law in question.

But many religious people still hold to the views which Jesus combated, and those who believe themselves to be more enlightened are often in no better case. Many believe that diseases could be prevented by a return to nature. I suppose that the first step in a return to nature would be the discarding of clothes, which would at once increase the mortality from pneumonia about a hundredfold. Of course, the phrase 'Live according to nature' is quite meaningless. Civilized and savage man, health and sickness, are equally parts of nature. Some features of civilization are bad for health, but for all that, such statistics as are available show that civilized men live longer than uncivilized. The same emotional drive forces people to believe that a cure must be available for most diseases. An acquaintance with the facts of medicine would show them that this is not so. Most disease can be prevented, but when it is there, in nine cases out of ten, the doctor can do very little but prescribe good nursing and rest.

As a matter of fact, the medical situation to-day is very serious. The expectation of life at birth is much the same in most civilized countries, and has risen for the last fifty years.

The greatest causes of this have been the abolition of water-borne diseases such as cholera, and the general prosperity which has nearly banished under-feeding as a cause of ill-health. To-day medical science is still advancing, but it is becoming harder and harder to apply its results in practice.

We know how to prevent infection with syphilis, but law and opinion forbid the spreading of this information, and the attempt to persuade the human race to avoid conduct likely to lead to infection has had little effect on the present generation. So syphilis goes on killing babies and filling asylums. We know how to cure most cases of cancer of the breast. This may seem a startling statement, but the official British medical statistics show that 91 per cent. of the cases of breast cancer, and half of the cases of uterine cancer, operated on at a sufficiently early stage five years ago are still alive and have had no recurrence of the disease. The prospects of radium treatment appear to be better still, but adequate figures are not yet available. Most of the victims of cancer in these sites die of it, however, because they do not go to the surgeon until they are in serious pain, by which time the cancer has spread and cannot be completely removed. In a series of European cases of uterine cancer the average time between onset of symptoms and consulting the doctor was about eight months. If any newspaper were to publish a daily warning of the early signs of cancer of the womb, it would save many lives, but would certainly lose in circulation, and probably be prosecuted for indecency.

The same thing is true of insulin. The worst sufferers from diabetes can regain full health and keep it indefinitely by two or three daily injections. But they cannot be got to realize this fact, because they have never been taught that their bodies are systems obeying quite definite laws, and a diabetic will no more work without insulin than a motor-car without lubricating oil. A medical friend recently had to deal with two women brought in dying of diabetes to the hospital where he worked. Both had been treated before, and taught to inject themselves twice daily with insulin. But one had broken her syringe and had not troubled to replace it at once, while the other had neglected her injections for two days because she was coming to hospital in any case for another complaint. Attitudes like this are so common that the discovery of insulin has made no appreciable difference to the mortality in England from diabetes. It has saved a few intelligent people, but that is all.

If a definitive cure for cancer is discovered in the next few years it is unlikely that it will be a simpler or safer affair than that of diabetes. If so, it will not have much effect on the mortality for several generations. In such a case any given person can no doubt flatter himself on belonging to the intelligent minority who will be saved. But if what science arrives at is not a cure, but a means of prevention, the case is even less hopeful. Experience has shown that in this respect individual action is almost useless. In a country where typhoid fever is common it is hard always to drink beer or wine, or personally to see that one's water is boiled; and annual inoculation involves a day's mild illness.* Typhoid infection can only be dealt with adequately by public control of the water supply, which involves no effect by individual citizens. Diphtheria, smallpox, measles, and other air-borne diseases could be stamped out by a public effort, but such an effort would involve the individual assistance and self-sacrifice of sick persons and their relatives, and also international co-operation. It is impossible until people realize that microbes are every bit as real as foreigners, and much more likely to kill one. They will only arrive at a sane view regarding disease as the result of a general education on scientific lines. The study of medicine apart from its scientific basis creates neurotics rather than scientists.

Preventive medicine could be made into the moral equivalent of war. It is already so for a few people. A colleague of mine was recently translating a French paper on chemotherapy when he came upon the phrase 'tué par l'ennemi' in reference to a deceased pharmacologist. 'I suppose', he said, 'that means that he died of an accidental infection.' I undeceived him; the enemy in this case had been the German nation; but his attitude was typical of medical scientists to-day. 'For we wrestle, not against flesh and blood, but against principalities, against powers, against the rulers of the darkness of this world.' St. Paul thought that the world was largely ruled by demons. We know better to-day, and we demand the general adoption of the scientific point of view because in its absence human effort is so largely devoted to conflicts with fellow-men, in which one, if

* Besredka's oral method of immunization, which has since been introduced, causes no illness.

not both, of the disputants must inevitably suffer. It is only in times of disaster that the average man devotes a moment's thought to his real enemies, 'the rulers of the darkness of this world' from bacteria to cyclones. Until humanity adopts the scientific point of view those enemies will not be conquered.

This adoption will inevitably be a slow process. But it will be quite unnecessarily slow unless those who desire it realize the nature of the opposition to it. One of the necessary pre-requisites is adequate biological teaching in schools. Such teaching will only be adequate if it brings biology into relation with daily life. In an agricultural community this would be possible by a study of agricultural plants and animals. In towns it can only come through the study of human anatomy and physiology, man being the only living organism familiar to the urban child. Any attempt to teach these subjects involves the violation of the most formidable taboos. Some of these still obstruct the teaching even of medical students.

The first of these taboos concerns human corpses. Every educated person should know what his or her inside looks like. Models and dead rabbits do not produce the necessary effect on the mind. It was not until I had attended a few post-mortems that I realized (with da Vinci, Wren, and others) that even the ugliest human exteriors may contain the most beautiful viscera, and was able to console myself for the facial drabness of my neighbours in omnibuses by dissecting them in my imagination. I do not suppose that I shall live to see this point of view generally adopted, but the first step towards it should be made by the prospective corpses. I feel no more personal interest in the disposal of my corpse or my wife's than of our old boots. They will therefore, I hope, be used as anatomical material.

The second objection is on religious grounds. It is impossible to reconcile our physiological knowledge with the curious fragments of archaic physiology which are imbedded here and there in religious doctrine. It may be possible for religion to discard them as it has discarded the solid-heaven theory. But many religious persons do not think so. Certainly the physiology of the brain is likely to prove as great a stumbling-block in this century as did the doctrine of evolution in the last.

The most serious opposition, however, comes from a third source. Human physiology is indecent. To take a simple example, it would be ridiculous to frame a practical course of that science which did not involve the analysis of urine, or a theoretical course which omitted the physiology of reproduction. Most people desire that thought on the latter subject should remain in the pre-scientific stage, and heavily charged with emotion. The emotion may vary in different cases. Some find it a subject for sentimentality, others for disgust, others, again, for humour. All agree in fearing an objective and scientific attitude to it, though this fear is rationalized in a number of different ways. As a consequence a considerable proportion of the rising generation is adopting a purely hedonistic standpoint on this topic. I think that those who are conservative in this matter should realize that, from their point of view, a biological attitude is preferable to a hedonistic. The biologist, for example, generally finds it improbable that a woman should find satisfaction in permanently interrupting the normal reproductive cycle so as to omit pregnancy and lactation, even though a low infantile mortality necessitates a certain degree of interference on social grounds.

For reasons such as these the educational preliminaries to a scientific point of view will meet with the most formidable resistances, largely unconscious. But until the scientific point of view is generally adopted, our civilization will continue to suffer from a fundamental disharmony. Its material basis is scientific, its intellectual framework is pre-scientific. The present state of the world suggests that unless a fairly vigorous attempt is made in the near future to remedy this disharmony, our particular type of civilization will undergo the fate of the cultures of the past. Those who consider that it is worth saving should realize the kind of effort which is necessary, and the kind of opposition which that effort will encounter.

THE INEQUALITY OF MAN

IT is a human characteristic to give reasons which will not bear examination for the most sensible actions. Many Polynesians are only kept from theft by the belief that if they violate the taboo attaching to the coco-nuts of their neighbours they will be struck dead. Some fundamentalists (at least in England) hold that a belief in Noah's ark is a necessary preliminary to a good life. In medieval Europe it was only possible to centralize government as a result of a belief in the divine institution of monarchy, which was later formulated as the divine right of kings.

And in the present age the admirable institution of universal suffrage is similarly supported by the curious dogma of the equality of man. Historically this dogma arose as a protest against institutions such as hereditary rank, which still commands the respect of the readers of the social columns of British newspapers and of the daughters of American millionaires. But if the framers of the American Constitution subscribed to the theory of the equality of man, the true founders of the nation, the Pilgrim Fathers, held the opposite doctrine in its most extreme form. They were Calvinists, and believed that human beings, from the moment of birth, were segregated into two distinct categories, the one predestined to eternal bliss, the other to everlasting damnation. A hundred per cent. American may therefore believe in equality with Washington and Paine, or in inequality with Winthrop and Bradford. I suspect that the truth lies somewhere between these two extremes.

Human inequality springs from two sources, nature and nurture. The results of the latter are obvious. It is no use appointing a man a clerk if he has not been taught to write, or a Christian missionary if he has been brought up as a Mohammedan. Two hundred years ago most inequality in Europe was due to this cause. To-day the same is true in Asia. Democracy is impossible in India to-day largely because less than 10 per cent. of its population can read. Hence Indian self-government would mean the rule of an Indian minority which would probably govern somewhat worse than the British. In China, too, universal education is a prerequisite of democracy. Some inequality due to differences of environment is inevitable, if only because of the facts of geography. But in its grosser forms it means an immense waste of human possibilities, and every progressive State aims at equality of opportunity. This phrase was invented, I believe, by the late Canon Rashdall, who attempted to teach me philosophy. Napoleon expressed the same idea by the motto 'La carrière ouverte aux talents', which stresses the inequality of human capacity, or talent. It was, of course, Jesus who converted the word 'talent' from the name for a sum of money to an expression for inborn human ability, of which he clearly recognized the existence.

For men are not born equal. No one disputes this fact as regards physical characteristics. Some babies are born black and some white, and very little can be done to alter the colour of the former. But just as in the United States some of the coloured people straighten their hair artificially, so, if a State should ever arise in which the ruling group is pigmented, it is possible that some of the whites will induce a permanent and bath-proof darkening of their skin by drinking a weak solution of silver nitrate. Even so their colour will be grey rather than mahogany. Many other characters are equally fixed. Provided a child is receiving an adequate diet, it is probably impossible to add an inch, let alone a cubit, to its stature. On the other hand, one could generally add a few pounds to its weight by overfeeding it. Children may be born without fingers, eyes, and so on, or with innumerable physical or chemical defects in their nature, which no amount of medical skill can overcome.

In the psychological realm things are the same. Everyone admits that a certain number of people are congenitally feeble-minded. But with regard to other mental and moral defects, ranging from stupidity and bad temper to lunacy and habitual criminality, the case is far less clear. The brothers and sisters of a family tend to resemble one another and their parents in intelligence, but it has been urged that, with the exception of a few congenital imbeciles, this resemblance is due to home influences, and not to heredity. The relative importance of heredity and home influences has recently been tested by Miss Burks in California. She compared the resemblances in intelligence of 200 children with their foster-parents, and of 100 children in the same schools with their true parents. The foster-children had been adopted at an average age of three months, so that home environment had had a fair chance. There was no definite relation between the intelligence rating of a child and its adopted father. The influence of the foster-mothers, though marked, was far less than that of the true fathers or mothers. There is a vast amount of further evidence to the same effect, for example, as to the great intellectual diversity of children in the same orphanage.

There is much less evidence with regard to moral character. No doubt some of the basal traits which determine it, such as quickness of response, are inherited, but it probably depends to a considerable extent on environment whether the quick-tempered child will develop into a fury or a kindly but impulsive person, the calmer personality into a heartless or a benevolent. This is largely a matter of common sense. Everyone knows that you can influence character far more easily than intelligence. That is why we apply physical or moral suasion to bad boys, but not to stupid ones unless we think they are lazy. But common sense is not contradicted by what little scientific evidence exists.

If you want to study the influence of environment on a plant, the best plan is to cut it in half and put the two halves in different soils. In spite of King Solomon, this experiment is rarely performed on children. But occasionally nature does something like it. Every now and then a pair of twins who resemble one another very closely are produced from a single cell. They are, of course, always of the same sex, and when brought up together grow up with similar habits and tastes. But what happens if they are brought up apart from birth? A few cases of this kind have been investigated. Professor Muller of Austin, Texas, described a case where two identical twin girls were separated at birth, owing to their mother's death. At thirty years of age their scores or intelligence tests were almost equal. Not one pair in a thousand of people taken at random would have been so similar. But other tests showed that the emotional side of their natures differed quite as much as those of two people taken at random. And their emotional lives had been quite different. One had married, the other was single; one was attracted by Catholicism, the other by Christian Science, and so on. Further studies of this kind will delimit the possibilities of social influence on the individual.*

To-day extreme eugenists proclaim that environment has very little influence, extreme behaviourists that nothing else matters. Dr. Watson finds that all healthy new-born babies behave pretty much alike, and deduces that the differences that develop as they grow up must be due to environment. This does not follow. All European babies are born blue-eyed, but it is not environment which determines their adult eye colour. In one of the plants with which I have worked, the Chinese primrose, almost all seedlings look alike, but with the genes at present available, several million easily distinguishable adult types could be built up. Actually a baby behaves in such a simple way because the nerve fibres in the upper part of his brain have not yet got sheaths of an oily substance called myelin, which probably acts as an insulator. It is not till the insulation is complete that mental differences due to brain structure can show up. No doubt environment counts for something, but the examples cited above tend to show that its field is limited. However, popular expositors of eugenics make the fundamental mistake of suggesting that differences not due to environment are due to heredity.

* Later work by Newman on similar twin pairs shows much greater intellectual differences than in Muller's case.

If this were true all children of the same two parents would be exactly alike in such characters as eye colour, which is not influenced by environment. It is quite true that heredity and environment between them determine almost all the differences which exist among self-fertilized plants like wheat, or animals such as dogs, in which man usually restricts matings to members of the same race. But cats, like men, usually choose their own mates, and are not influenced in doing so by eugenical considerations. In consequence very few cats are pure-blooded, or in scientific terminology, homozygous, for the genes producing colour. Two tabbies may produce tabby, black, blue, and white spotted kittens in a single litter. The cause of this variety is called segregation. It is simply a name for the fact that the cross-bred cat distributes different genes to its various children.

In a human population within which marriages take place freely, segregation and heredity account for almost exactly the same amount of inequality in such characters as stature, eye colour, and intellectual abilities. In other words, the inequality of two brothers with the same ancestry is on the average about half that of two men taken at random. But in a population where different groups breed among themselves the influence of heredity is of course greater. Two Chinese will not produce white, or nearly white, children, simply because they have no white ancestors. But two short stupid parents may produce a tall clever child because they probably include some tall clever people among their very mixed ancestry.

Now we cannot at present control segregation, except to a small extent, but we can and do control heredity in animal and plant breeding, and could in human

C

society if eugenics became a reality. That is why eugenics is at present the only possible way of improving the innate characters of man. But for all that, biology does not support the idea that the hereditary principle is a satisfactory method of choosing men or women to fill a post. Segregation sees to it that very few human characters breed true. The average degree of resemblance between father and son is too small to justify the waste of human potentialities which an hereditary aristocratic system entails. If human beings could be propagated by cutting, like apple trees, aristocracy would be biologically sound. England would presumably be governed by cuttings of Cromwell and Chatham; America, as I believe Bateson once suggested, by cuttings of Washington and Lincoln. But until the art of tissue culture has developed very considerably, such possibilities need not even be thought of.

The progress of biology in the next century will lead to a recognition of the innate inequality of man. This is to-day most obviously visible in the United States, where educational opportunities are more widespread than elsewhere. Universal education leads, not to equality, but to inequality based on real differences of talent. Where there is equality of opportunity there is no excuse for failure. The self-made American successful man who realizes this fact, commonly appears ruthless to the European aristocrat, who, just because he knows that he does not owe his position to innate ability, is often more considerate to his inferiors. If hereditary wealth were abolished, the tendency would, of course, be strengthened. So some observers see in the Russian Communist Party the germ of the proudest, most efficient and most ruthless aristocracy that the world has ever seen. Personally I doubt the validity of such a forecast so long as the party continues to hold to its present economic and political doctrines, and to enforce upon its members the principle of a maximum income at present about £270 per year.

The social danger of a system which, in practice if not in theory, gives so full a recognition to inequality, is that it tends to estimate that inequality too simply. In America the tendency is strong to grade men and women primarily by their earning power. A Socialist Government would try to grade them by their economic value to the State. The Catholic Church attempts to assess them by their share of those virtues which it admires, the principal classes being saints, other saved souls, and damned. University professors gradually come to believe that the sheep can infallibly be separated from the goats by a series of written examinations. And there are psychologists who believe that it is possible to grade everyone by means of intelligence tests. The best known of these tests is that applied to the American army in 1917. Success or failure in these tests undoubtedly depends less on education than success or failure in ordinary examinations. They are, therefore, a better test of innate inequality. But what do they measure? This is the question which Spearman, Aveling, Thompson, and other English psychologists are trying to answer. They take a number of boys and girls who have had so far as possible the same educational opportunities, and compare their performances in a number of different simple tests. It is found that the performances of the same child in some tests, for example, detection of absurdities and memorization of sentences, are clearly related to one another; in others, for example, memory of form and interpretation of pictures, only slightly related either to one another or to those in any other subject. And this rule is general. If one sort of ability helps one to predict any other sort, it helps one to predict all sorts. The only exceptions were in the case of very similar performances, such as various different types of arithmetic. But such exceptions are rather rare. The theory was therefore framed that ability to perform any task was the sum of two abilities—general ability, which is required to a greater or lesser degree for all purposes; and a special ability, different for each type of performance. On this basis general ability can be measured, of course on an arbitrary scale, as the result of a mathematical process. The theory of this measurement has given rise to a series of somewhat heated mathematical discussions, of which one of the most intelligible is based on the geometry of figures in space of sixteen or so dimensions. Whether the number 'g' at which Spearman arrives really represents general intellectual ability or not it is fairly closely related to success in intellectual pursuits. But the relation is one-sided. For example, all successful university students have a high 'g', but not all students with high 'g' are successful. A large number, at least, of these failures fail because they are lazy, or at least do not work at the subjects prescribed.

The educational systems of the world appear to be based on a very simple fallacy about 'g'. It is better measured by linguistic ability than by mathematical; for mathematics, like music or drawing, demands a considerable amount of a special ability, in addition to the ability measured by 'g'. Hence it is a commonplace of universities that men who have obtained classical scholarships are likely to do well in science and other subjects, while mathematical scholars more rarely succeed outside their own speciality. It is supposed therefore that the classics are a magnificent training for the mind. It is quite true that when two boys have spent ten years in learning Latin, unprepared translation from that language furnishes quite a good test of their general ability combined with a capacity for rather dull work. Probably, however, a set of cross-word puzzles would be as good, and a set of simple psychological tests much better.

There is, however, no evidence at all that classical or any other education increases 'g', and a good deal that it does not. Heliotherapy is the only procedure which is quite certainly known to increase it! But the removal of tonsils and adenoids probably does so. It seems to be fairly strongly inherited, and education can do little more than just give it a chance to show up.

General ability is only the most important of a series of psychological traits which can be measured with more or less accuracy. Fortunately, some of the others are far more readily influenced by environment. In the course of the next century, if psychologists are allowed anything like a free hand, and co-operate with geneticists, it should be possible by the time a child is about seven to arrive at a fair idea of its capacities, and children will be sorted out accordingly. To-day we often have special schools for mentally deficient children, and occasionally for very able ones. This system will, of course, be greatly extended. When children of all grades of ability are combined in one class, the intelligent merely learn to be lazy while the stupid are hopelessly discouraged. And the attempt to remedy this defect by placing children of widely different ages in the same class is also a failure. I do not think, for example, that my intellect has improved appreciably since I was twelve years old, though I have learned a great deal since that time and can work for longer hours. But I doubt if my ability to deal with a really new type of problem has increased. As I am now cleverer than most boys of eighteen I probably was so then, and intellectual differences would not have been equalized by putting me into a class with them.

The world is crammed with experimental schools, and as a university teacher I notice no very great difference between men who have been educated by quite different methods. The most important experiment, to my mind, would be to start a school whose membership was confined to really intelligent children. Such children could easily reach the standards of the average university graduate at eighteen. I did so myself, because I was fortunate enough to go to Eton at a time when the curriculum was so completely disorganized that it was possible with a little effort to learn either a great deal or nothing at all. Now, however, I understand that the courses are arranged to fit the average boy, and it is a good deal harder for the intelligent to learn more than his fellows.

But, of course, general ability is only one of many innate psychological characteristics in which children differ. Musical, mathematical, and artistic abilities are largely congenital. Poets also are commonly held to be born, not made. One of the most urgent tasks of the psychologist is to pick out the budding poets from the embryonic painters, plumbers, politicians, pedagogues, and so on. At present vocational selection is a very rudimentary art, and it generally takes place at the end, not near the beginning, of education. There is a curious notion abroad that the progress of science is likely to reduce humanity to a common dull level. This may conceivably be true of physics and chemistry, but I believe that the opposite is the case with biology and psychology. The same hypothetical accusation is made against Socialism, yet I have never seen such diversity, of clothes at any rate, as in the streets of Moscow, where one can wear anything but a top hat; though I unfortunately missed the famous occasion when a band of Communist youth of both sexes appeared in mid-winter clad in red ribbons bearing the Russian equiva-lent of 'Down with shame'.

In a scientifically ordered society innate human diver-sity would be accepted as a natural phenomenon like the weather, predictable to a considerable extent, but very difficult to control. In England one person in two hundred is feeble-minded, and perhaps as many more cannot be of much use to their fellows owing to con-genital blindness, deafness, and other inborn defects. The other 99 per cent. could probably all be of social value. In the words of Professor Spearman:* 'Every normal man, woman and child is a genius at something, as well as an idiot at something. It remains to discover what—at any rate in respect of the genius.'

The scientific State would make it its first business to investigate this problem. The development of an ade-quate technique would be a matter of generations, as was the development of chemical analysis. It would enable the individual to follow his or her own bent far more completely than is now possible. Education would

* *The Abilities of Man.* (Macmillan.)

probably be more specialized for the average child, but the exceptionally versatile would not be compelled, as they now are, to limit the field of their studies at an early stage. In the absence of such a technique the State can do very little. The only clear task of eugenics is to prevent the inevitably inefficient one per cent. of the population from being born, and to encourage the breeding of persons of exceptional ability where that ability is known to be hereditary. We cannot as yet go much further than this. We do not know whether the sporadically appearing man or woman of genius is substantially more likely to produce children of genius than the average intelligent person. We do not know if a society containing too many intelligent people would not be unstable. Such a cause may have brought about the downfall of Athens. At best, eugenics would have no effect for a generation. Vocational guidance would begin to act at once. It should be added that vocational guidance, as often practised for profit to-day, is generally about as useful as astrology, without possessing the charming vocabulary and distinguished past of the latter pseudo-science. We are only in possession of a part of the scientific data needed to make it a practical proposition. But even now a few vocational guidance institutes are doing useful work.

I do not believe that a recognition of the inequality of man would be a blow to democracy (or rather to representative government based on universal suffrage). This admirable invention is a device for changing the government of a country without a revolution. It is successful because it gives a fairly good approximation to the result which would be obtained by a civil war, provided that a majority of the people take politics seriously. For example, the British Labour Party can at present only persuade about a third of the electors to support them. Hence the few revolutionaries who are included amongst its many supporters realize that they would be beaten in a civil war. If the party polled a majority of votes and were prevented by the King or Lords from carrying out their policy, a revolution would command enough support to make it at least worth attempting. Hence, the King is unlikely to veto the legislation of a Labour Government supported by a majority of voters, though the Lords will try to delay it.

The danger to democracy to-day lies not in the recognition of a plain biological fact, but in a lack of will in certain countries to kill persons who obstruct the declared wishes of the majority of the people. Charles I. died and Mussolini lives because enough Englishmen wanted to kill the former, but not enough Italians want to kill the latter. This lack of will may arise from mere laziness, or, more frequently, from disillusion at the results of representative democracy, which is presumably not the ideal form of government, but only the best so far invented. Unless the mass of the people are willing in the last resort to fight for their convictions, democracy should be replaced by the government of a minority, whether of Fascists, Communists, or what not, who possess that will.

It is, of course, irrational that each man's vote should possess equal value. But the alternatives so far tried or suggested are still less rational. They usually take the form of increasing the political power of those who are wealthy enough to be able to influence politics already. One eminently desirable reform would be the disfranchisement of persons over sixty-five years of age.

The main effects of their votes will not appear during their lifetime; they would be useless in a civil war, and their political views depend on issues of a generation ago. In England our old men and women vote for a protective tariff because they were formerly opposed to Irish Home Rule, in America because their childish sympathies in the Civil War were for the North!

Some day it may be possible to devise a scientific method of assessing the voting power of individuals. One can be fairly certain that that day is more than a century ahead. In the remote future mankind may be divided into castes like Hindus or termites. But to-day the recognition of innate inequality should lead not to less, but to greater, equality of opportunity.

SCIENTIFIC CALVINISM

I LIKE philosophers, and I believe that they fulfil a function of great importance. There are a very large number of questions with regard to which there is no satisfactory evidence, and it is important that they should be considered as open. Now agnosticism is an intellectual tight-rope which most people cannot tread for long. The majority of adults in all civilized countries seem to be fairly clear that Socialism either would or would not increase human happiness. They do this on *a priori* grounds, quite regardless of the fact that Socialism has nowhere been tried. Even in Russia, though industry has on the whole been socialized (and is working fairly successfully), the vast majority of the population is engaged in individualistic agriculture (which is not doing well).* Until Russian agriculture has been socialized and the results noted, there will be no conclusive evidence that Socialism is practicable or impracticable, let alone desirable or undesirable.

When philosophical proof or disproof of any proposition is brought forward, we can be fairly sure that there is no cogent evidence as to its truth. We know a good deal more about iron than about God. It should be quite possible to bring forward *a priori* arguments showing that a lump of iron unsupported by anything but air is very likely to fall to the ground. But as far as I know, philosophers rarely do this, though they devote

* This was, of course, written before the socialization of agriculture.

much attention to proving the precise nature of divine omnipotence. To my mind the most valuable function of philosophers is to be professional doubters. But for philosophers no one would have thought of doubting all kinds of apparently obvious, but actually far-from-certain propositions, such as the independent reality of matter.

One of the real signs of human progress is that certain questions are from time to time taken out of the philosophers' hands and settled. In the Middle Ages the existence of antipodes was constantly being disproved. As these debates were not broadcast, the Maoris never learned of their non-existence. A hundred years ago Hegel was explaining why there could only be seven planets. Wolff discovered thirty-one new planets in the first three months of 1928. The freedom of the will is still a question for philosophers, but I suspect that within the next generation it will be taken out of their hands. This doctrine has been a subject of vehement debate since Calvin adopted the Muslim doctrine of predestination in opposition to the Catholics and many Protestant Christians. The progress of science has added arguments on both sides. Determinism, until about ten years ago, had furnished extraordinarily satisfactory explanations of physical and biological phenomena, and as the will finds its expression in definite physical and biological occurrences, it was natural to extend the principle of determinism to cover willed as well as unwilled events. The naïve idea of the will is a force driving the body to action. One cannot disprove the existence of such a force, for it is generally very difficult to prove negative propositions by scientific methods. But it has been shown that a man produces the same amount of energy, within a fifth of one per cent., as would a machine using his food as fuel. I have no doubt that, with sufficient care, the agreement could be made very much closer.

On the other hand, the doctrine of evolution lent some support to the opposite point of view. If man has evolved from animals of a lower mental organization mainly as the result of natural selection, it is difficult to see why his consciousness should have evolved if it is merely a looker-on in the game, and cannot actively influence events. This, to be sure, is an argument against materialistic determinism rather than against a determinism such as that of Calvin. In the last three years a far more important assault has been made on determinism by Heisenberg and other physicists. They claim that while causality applies to large bodies, it does not apply to atoms. One cannot say that an atom in a given situation will behave in such and such a manner, merely that there is a certain probability that it will do so. But if we observe a body containing as few as a million million atoms (which requires a powerful microscope), these probabilities coalesce to a practical certainty. In a million million bridge hands the odds against a one per cent. excess of black cards is over ten thousand million million to one. The odds against a one per cent. deviation from the ordinary laws of mechanics by a particle large enough to be seen with a microscope are about as large. Hence indeterminism for atoms involves practical determinism for large bodies, even if atomic events are really independent of one another, which seems to be the case. As the principle of atomic indeterminism enables an accurate prediction of all sorts of previously incalculable events, it is being very widely adopted by physicists.

Eddington, in his Gifford lectures on *The Nature of the Physical World*, has attempted to identify this atomic indeterminism with the freedom of the will. He regards the human body as a device, so to say, for magnifying its effects from the atomic to the visible scale of magnitude. There is, so far as one can see, nothing impossible in this point of view. It accords with our more primitive notions as to our own behaviour, which may quite well contain an element of truth. But it is of no obvious help to the physiologist. His task is to explain how the organism obeys various laws which are not obviously obeyed by lifeless matter, and exhibits a kind of unity not shown by a machine. It is not clear how a certain laxity in obeying mechanical laws will help to explain implicit obedience to physiological laws.

Unfortunately Eddington goes on to arguments of a less scientific character. 'The materialist', he says, '. . . must presumably hold the belief that his wife is a rather elaborate differential equation, but he is probably tactful enough not to obtrude this opinion in domestic life.' I recently put this point to a happily married physicist of my acquaintance. He replied that he would not love his wife if he did not believe that she was a differential equation, or rather that her conduct obeyed one. He loves her because she has a definite character which renders her conduct intelligible even when it is surprising. And in this she certainly resembles a differential equation. There are dull differential equations just as there are dull wives. There are others, such as Schrödinger's wave equation, which is at the bottom of a great deal of modern physics, that lead to the most odd and beautiful results. Men have fallen in love with statues and pictures. I find it far easier to imagine a man falling in love with a differential equation, and I am inclined to think that some mathematicians have done so. Even in a non-mathematician like myself, some differential equations evoke fairly violent physical sensations similar to those described by Sappho and Catullus when viewing their mistresses. Personally, however, I obtain an even greater 'kick' from finite difference equations, which are perhaps more like those which an up-to-date materialist would use to describe human behaviour.

I do not believe, then, that we are likely to arrive at any solution of the problem except by a scientific study of human behaviour. If we wanted to disprove the existence of free-will in machines, we could do one of two things. We could place the same machine in as nearly as possible the same environment twice over, and compare its behaviour. This method is inapplicable to men, because they learn from experience in a way which most machines do not. I say most machines, because it would be possible to construct a machine which learned. For example, there is a kind of toy clockwork beetle which can be made to run about a table. By means of its metal antennae which project in front of it, its motion is altered just before it reaches the edge, and consequently it does not fall off. A further refinement could be added so that the safety mechanism did not work till the beetle had once or twice fallen off the table.

The second method of research would be to compare the behaviour of two very similar machines in very similar circumstances. Of course we could not make two machines exactly identical, nor their environments. So perhaps once in ten thousand times the behaviour of the two machines would diverge for no ascertainable cause.

The ghost of Samuel Butler, who thought very highly of the abilities of machines, could claim that they exhibited free-will once in ten thousand experiments. More ordinary minds would regard such divergences in behaviour as unimportant. Now this method is applicable to human beings.

No two human beings are exactly alike, but some pairs are so nearly alike that, quite literally, their own mother cannot tell them apart. Twins are often of different sexes, and, if so, resemble one another no more than ordinary brothers and sisters. Most twins of the same sex are no more alike. But rather more than one-third of twins of the same sex resemble one another to an extreme degree. This is most easily shown with regard to physical characters. Their stature and colouring are extremely alike. Their finger-prints are generally distinguishable, but those of the right hand of one of them are more like those of his brother's right hand than of his own left. It has been known since the time of Galton that when they were brought up in the same environment their moral and intellectual characters were extraordinarily similar. Identical twins (as these very similar twins are inaccurately called) appear to be derived from the same fertilized egg, and hence carry the same particular group of hereditary factors contributed by the parents. They resemble one another as do cuttings of the same plant, while ordinary twins differ just as do seedlings from the same plant, provided that it does not belong to a pure race.

The differences between human beings can all be ascribed to four causes. The first cause is difference of ancestry. In most cases a black man is black and a white man white because they resemble their parents. The second is segregation, which causes congenital differences between children with the same ancestry. The third cause is difference of environment. This includes, for example, difference of education, injury, exposure to disease, divine grace, diabolical temptation, or any other supernatural interference, and so on. The fourth cause is freedom of the will, or any other events not determined by the past. It may turn out that the fourth cause is non-existent, like the snakes of Ireland, but it would be unscientific to assume this, except as a provisional working hypothesis.

Now if we compare an ordinary pair of brothers brought up in the same family we have eliminated the first of our four causes and a good deal of the third, but the second remains, and we know that as regards stature it accounts for about as much variation as the first. When we compare 'identical' twins we have eliminated the first two causes completely. The investigation now takes two different paths. In the first place, we can study identical twins who have been separated at birth. This is one of the most satisfactory methods available of estimating the relative importance of nature and nurture. Only four* such pairs have yet received adequate study. They show already that nurture makes a good deal more difference than extreme eugenists suppose, a fact very favourable to those who base great hopes on the improvement of human environment. The emotional side of the mind seems to be somewhat more plastic than the intellectual, as I think might be expected from the results of modern psychology. But any deductions from such data must be entirely provisional until far more are available.

* Since the above was written, Prof. Newman has raised this number to ten.

D

The other line of investigation is that of identical twins brought up in the same environment. Here we have eliminated our first and second causes of difference, and a good deal of the third. Differences between such 'identical' twins are partly due to the accidental diversities which occur in their experience, partly, perhaps, to freedom of the will. Now the freedom of the will is supposed, by Catholic and other moralists, to operate particularly in the choice between good and bad actions. Our twins might resemble one another in intellectual habits, tricks of speech, and so on, and yet show independence in their moral decisions.

The first satisfactory data for deciding the possible importance of free-will in determining conduct are furnished in Professor Lange's book, *Verbrechen als Schicksal* (*Crime as Destiny*),* published in 1929. It is only ninety-six pages in length, but it is quite conceivable that posterity will regard it as the most important book of this century.

Prof. Lange, with the help of the Bavarian Ministry of Justice and the authorities of some of the South German states, investigated every available case in which a criminal was one of a pair of living twins of the same sex. Both members of the pair, where possible, were investigated by physical and psychological methods. In addition the criminality or otherwise of the adult non-twin brothers of 428 male criminals was summarily investigated. About one in twelve of these was a criminal.

The twins fall into two groups. Sixteen pairs are physically no more like than ordinary brothers. In fifteen such pairs one brother, and one only, is a criminal. In the sixteenth both are so, but one is an habitual

* Translated by my wife in 1931 (Allen & Unwin).

criminal with an aggregate of over eighteen years of sentences. The other had gone off the rails during a period of one year, and then kept straight for fifteen. One pair of twins, probably, but not certainly, 'identical', and not closely examined, is classified with the unlike twins owing to this doubt. Both were criminals, but one was a habitual swindler; the other had once been imprisoned for three days for petty theft. Thus at most the unlike twins showed about the same resemblance in respect of crime as ordinary brothers. Two out of seventeen agreed in being criminals.

With the 'identical' pairs the case is very different. Thirteen pairs were investigated. Ten of these pairs were both criminals. In the other three cases only one had been convicted. The stories of the ten concordant pairs are given in great detail. On the whole there is an extraordinary agreement between the behaviour of pairs. First come a pair of habitual burglars, then two weak-willed brothers who had occasionally been guilty of petty theft. Neither had ever collaborated in crime with his twin.

Four pairs started life with juvenile crimes of petty violence or theft, generally under the influence of alcohol. Two of these pairs are still young. The other two are older, and in both cases have diverged. In each case one brother has married a woman with sufficient character to keep man and wife 'straight'; the other has been less fortunate, and has lived on his wife's immoral earnings in the intervals of theft.

Two pairs of twin brothers were swindlers. But one pair made large fortunes quite independently before they were found out; the other merely collaborated in a 'business' which kept no accounts and ended in a fraudulent bankruptcy. Another pair of twin brothers were both guilty of the same type of sexual abnormality. The only pair of female twins were not serious criminals, but their sexual experience was so excessively variegated that it was inevitable that they should ultimately fall into the hands of the police, the one for refusing to disclose the address of a thief who had been her lover, the other (on rather slight grounds) for keeping a disorderly house. Except for their extreme promiscuity the two sisters are blameless, being both honest and industrious.

Of the three criminal 'identical' twins whose brothers are not criminal, one murdered his sweetheart in a quarrel, one embezzled. His brother's circumstances at the time of the crime were entirely different as the result of a severe wound during the war. The third case is more surprising. One twin is apparently normal sexually, the other is a homosexual, and certain of his physical characteristics are slightly feminine. This fact may be due to an injury received at birth, which caused, among other things, a slight facial paralysis.

To sum up, differences of environment and free-will together saved only three out of thirteen twins from imitating their criminal brother or sister. The differences were sometimes fairly considerable. Two of the criminal twins had been separated at eight years of age. Another pair, who parted somewhat later, both ran away from their jobs at the same moment when over a hundred miles apart, and later developed acute appendicitis on almost the same day when even further separated. The one influence that appears to be important is that of women. Two criminals were reformed by their wives; the brother of a normal man murdered his sweetheart.

These twins only form a sample. It may be a slightly misleading sample. The odds are many millions to one that it is not wholly misleading. We may take it that in the course of a century similar data will have accumulated for thousands of pairs of twins. It will then be possible to say with certainty that at least 80 per cent. (or some such figure) of these moral decisions that land us in gaol or otherwise are predetermined. A more scientific analysis, on the lines marked out by Freud, of the effects on character of infantile experience, will probably serve to whittle down still further the possible field of indeterminism. In fact every educated person will be substantially a determinist in ethics as he now is in physics where individual atoms are not concerned. One may remark that Kant's loophole of escape from predestination will be barred. He admitted that the various events in a human life were determined, but allowed the soul a transcendental freedom which affected the character as a whole. But if two twins from the same egg are obliged to choose the same character little remains of such a freedom. The utmost latitude allowable for the will is, in the words of Mr. J. S. Dunne, who in *An Experiment with Time* has produced the most original theory of its freedom known to me, to assume that in relation to the brain it is 'analogous, not to a skilled musician composing with the aid of a piano, but to the amateur user of a pianola, whose interference with the complicated performances of that instrument is limited to the changing of one perforated roll for another'.

What will be the effect on society of the acceptance of determinism as a practical belief, even if a small area is left for freedom, like the Indian reservations in the United States? Two great religions, Islam and Calvinism, have held this belief. Both have produced extremely fine characters. The good Calvinist feels that God's grace will certainly keep him good, and this belief is an immense source of strength. The narrowness of both these religions is due to the fact that God, who created men with all kinds of characters, is only supposed to approve of one particular kind. Hence the unstable type of humanity which has produced so much great art has a far better chance under the other forms of Christianity than under Calvinism.

When the late William Bateson, the greatest geneticist whom England has so far produced, was lecturing during the war on the innate differences of mankind, a Scottish soldier said to him, 'Sir, what you're telling us is nothing but scientific Calvinism'. Will scientific Calvinism produce the same type of society and individual character as religious Calvinism? It is quite possible. Many eugenists devote a large part of their energies to disapproving of their fellow-creatures. Other calvinistically minded social reformers believe that society can only be saved by abolishing conditions, such as the sale of alcoholic drinks, which are stumbling-blocks to men of a certain constitution. Of the ten pairs of criminal twins, two or three would probably have escaped criminality in a society where alcohol and narcotic drugs were unobtainable.

There is, however, quite a different possibility, which appealed to Bateson. If innate human diversity is an ineradicable fact, the ideal society is one in which as many types as possible can develop in accordance with their possibilities. So far every society has tended to idealize one particular type. Some have been narrower than others. The immense strength of Catholicism lies largely in its doctrine of vocation, according to which a man or woman may be called by God to any of a large variety of careers, and please him in any of them. Hinduism has a very similar doctrine. Unfortunately neither of these religions is whole-hearted in the matter. Both place the calling of saint in a peculiar position, and in the Catholic Church all sorts of abnormal conduct, such as celibacy, have long been considered a pre-requisite of sanctity.

A young civilization tends to be less tolerant of diversity than an old. A violent and successful political or social change often standardizes admiration of a particular type. The Italian Fascist models himself on a certain strong though by no means silent man. The American borne aloft on an immense wave of com-mercial prosperity idealizes the capitalists and inventors who have organized that prosperity. In certain stable communities a more tolerant attitude prevails. Under the third French Republic it is probable that more different human types are encouraged than in any other society. Let us take seven human beings who have achieved fame under it: Pasteur, Renan, Anatole France, Marshal Foch, Ste. Thérèse de l'Enfant Jesus, Sarah Bernhardt, and Suzanne Lenglen. I doubt whether any other State could produce a team quite so thoroughly representative of the different sides of human nature. In England, for example, certain of Anatole France's works would have been suppressed on the ground of indecency, and Ste. Thérèse would have found con-siderable difficulty in being saintly when alive, and almost insuperable obstacles to performing well-attested miracles after her death.

It is unnecessary to add that France, in spite of this

immense diversity of human types, possesses as characteristic a culture and as high a degree of national unity in times of crisis as any other State.

There is, after all, something to be said for human diversity. If we believe that God created the world, he is very clearly responsible for the innate differences between men. Popular wisdom is sympathetic with the creator, realizing that 'it takes all sorts to make a world'. Religions other than Taoism appear to agree in setting up a single ideal for all men. Perhaps, however, the man in the street is in this respect nearer to God than the clergyman. Incidentally, in so far as we succeed in loving our neighbour, we love him as he is, not as he ought to be. This extremely difficult feat engenders a healthy respect for human diversity. If we reject any supernatural standard of values we inevitably make man the measure of all things. We clearly cannot take any particular man, such as Jesus, Mohammed, Newton, or Bach, for our only measure. At most we can reject a certain number of human types as unsuited for life in any possible community. Apart from this, the ideal society and the ideal system of ethics will allow the development of as many types as possible.

It appears then that the acceptance of determinism may be expected to lead to either of two types of society. England has generally been a tolerant country. It made some of the earliest steps towards religious freedom after the tyranny of the Reformation and counter-Reformation. As I come to the study of society from that of genetics, it is natural enough that I should be prejudiced in favour of human diversity and should hope that my country will not try to suppress it. But I should hesitate to brand those of the opposite opinion as unscientific, even if I think them inhuman.

It is fairly obvious that a belief in determinism (or shall we say 99 per cent. determinism) would profoundly modify our attitude to crime, but it would only speed up present tendencies. Already the attitude of most enlightened people to crime is that punishment should be a deterrent to the criminal and others rather than a retribution, and should where possible include an attempt to reform the criminal. Moral indignation is regarded as out-of-date. It has its uses, but it is the finest known excuse for cruelty, just as cruelty is the best excuse for moral indignation. This is well exemplified in the correspondence columns of our Press, where dear old ladies who can no longer attend witch-burnings write to demand torture (usually flogging) as a punishment for cruelty to animals. It has had its uses in the past, before law began to supersede vengeance. It is now a dangerous vestige like the vermiform appendix. I have had the latter removed, but I regret to say that my bosom often swells with moral indignation against all kinds of people whom it would be more rational to pity for their conduct.

A certain fraction of human conduct is largely controllable by social pressure, and praise and blame are effective means of controlling it. They prevent a large number of bad actions. But they do not, as it seems to me, involve any particular view as to the freedom of the will. They are part of the environment which determines our actions. Every crime represents a failure of society to control a criminal, as well as a failure on the part of the criminal to respond to social control. We do not at present know enough of biology to alter the structure of the criminal's brain and mind; or to prevent potential criminals being born; we must take him as we find him, and attempt so to order society that he does not commit crime.

In some countries, such as the United States, much remains to be done to make the criminal law an effective deterrent. In England this end has been largely accomplished, and a good deal is being done to reform criminals so that they do not repeat their offence. But we could still do much to diminish crime in two ways. In the first place, we could cease to punish various forms of abnormal conduct, especially sexual conduct, which are now criminal, and which, though inelegant, do no harm except perhaps to the criminals. The example of such countries as Denmark proves that a relaxation of the law in these matters would not be dangerous. Secondly, we can alter the law so that crime is not the only practicable escape from an intolerable situation. To-day theft is often the only method available for supplying one's children with boots, and murder or suicide the only way of terminating a marriage with an habitual criminal or drunkard.

Britain is ripe to-day for a new attitude to crime based on scientific data and a scientific point of view. The great reforms of a century ago in our criminal law, which abolished capital punishment for minor offences, resulted from the partial adoption of utilitarianism. A similar reform would be only one of the many benefits which would result from the general adoption of a more scientific point of view regarding human conduct.

IS HISTORY A FRAUD?

EVERY generation must re-write history. New facts become available, and old facts are interpreted anew. In the last century several new standpoints have been adopted, and in particular the attempt has been made to interpret history in terms of economics. But the greatest change has been in the extent of history. A hundred years ago it began about 700 B.C. Before that time there were various legends. Those of the Bible were in a class apart, and they were treated as Sacred history, and put into a separate compartment from Profane, or ordinary history. As long as one was compelled to believe in the literal truth of two mutually contradictory accounts of the great Mesopotamian flood, it was no use trying to disentangle the very considerable amount of historical fact embedded in these legends. And the effort of faith involved was relieved by a quite undue scepticism about other legendary events with a historical core, such as the siege of Troy and the story of the Minotaur.

The enlargement of our horizon began with the interpretation of Egyptian hieroglyphics. If Columbus doubled the field of geography by discovering America, Champollion in 1821 doubled the field of history by making possible the translation of documents some of which are over 4000 years old. A generation later Rawlinson decoded the cuneiform script in which the languages of ancient Mesopotamia were inscribed on clay tablets. As a result of this, history now extends

more than twice as far into the past as it did a century
ago. It is true that the earliest date known with certainty is 2283 B.C. At 11 A.M. on March 8 of that year
occurred a total eclipse of the sun, which portended the
sack of Ur by the Elamites. This ended the third
dynasty of Ur, a city whose history at that time went
back to before Noah's flood, which had not completely
submerged it, though it laid down 6 feet of mud in its
low-lying suburbs. The date of the flood is still doubtful, though probably somewhere between 4000 and
5000 B.C. On the other hand, Woolley is quite con-
fident as to the main sequence of events in southern
Mesopotamia as far back as about 3500 B.C., though the
dates may well be a century out. Egyptian history
appears to begin rather later than this.

Where there are no written or carved records it has
been possible to construct a very rough picture of the
more important events. Thus we have evidence, from
sudden changes in the shapes of the skulls in graves and
the objects found with them, of two prehistoric inva-
sions of England. And still further back one discovers,
though only in their dimmest outlines, a whole series
of different stone ages, each with its characteristic skull-
shape and art, until one reaches the half-men of Neanderthal, with great brow-ridges and no chins. They
chipped flints in a crude way, and possessed fire, but,
though they inhabited Europe for scores of thousands
of years, they have not left a single work of art. Only
by a perhaps misplaced courtesy do we call them men.
It is against this background of barbarism that history
stands out.

As history cannot exist in the absence of records, and
as archaeology has already reached back to the origin

of writing, from pictures, both in Egypt and Mesopotamia, it is unlikely that future research will ever extend our historical knowledge very much further into the past. We shall probably never know the name of any man, city, or nation, before 5000 B.C. Most of historical research in the future will consist in the filling in of gaps. It is therefore possible to-day for the first time to take a bird's-eye view of history as a whole.

The picture so obtained proves, I think, that the history taught to-day in our schools and universities is reliable in its details, but as a whole quite misleading. English history is taught as a progress in social organization, broken only by the decay of Roman civilization and its final overthrow by the Angles and Saxons. And the origins of our culture are traced back, on the one hand to the Greeks and Romans, who gradually built up a complete civilization with highly developed literature, art, and law, from rude beginnings; on the other to the Jews, who evolved most of the religious and ethical ideas which govern us to-day.

The truth is rather different. The curtain rises at Ur and other cities of the land then called Sumer in southern Mesopotamia, about 3500 B.C., and reveals a fully developed civilization. They built well, using the arch, which only reached Europe 3000 years later. They had cloth, wheeled vehicles, pottery, bronze, copper, silver and gold ware, a small amount of iron, sculpture, music, writing (on clay tablets), seals, and a complete social organization. And it is unfortunately quite clear to anyone who visited the British museum in 1928 that their standard of taste in art was superior to our own to-day. They still killed servants to wait on dead princes in Kur-nu-gea (No Return Land), but this practice had been abandoned 500 years later. Though one cannot defend this custom, it is only fair to remember that in this enlightened age more people were killed in four years as a result of the death of the Archduke Franz Ferdinand than were sacrificed in the whole course of Sumerian history. When we get a clearer view of their civilization, about 2500 B.C., we find sanitary conveniences with adequate drains in the houses, better than those of many English cottages to-day. There was a small standing army supported by a feudal system, with conscription in time of emergency for citizens. Slaves existed, but had some legal rights, and could own property. So could women, married or unmarried. There was a definite code of civil and criminal law, with professional judges. 4500 years ago southern Mesopotamia was a great deal more civilized than is half the world to-day. Egypt was also civilized, though probably the average man or woman was worse off than in Mesopotamia. There was also a civilization in the valley of the Indus, of which we know very little, except that it must have been in contact, or have had a common origin, with that of Mesopotamia.

We do not yet know where civilization started. The Mesopotamians said that their ancestors came from the sea, that is the Persian Gulf. As they represented their gods as standing on mountains, it is conjectured that they came from a hilly country. Their culture cannot have come mainly from Egypt as is sometimes believed, unless some very serious mistakes indeed have been made with regard to dates.

At present the principal clue to the spot where civilization began comes from an entirely unexpected source, namely, plant genetics. Civilization is based, not only on men but on plants and animals. It needs a cultivated plant giving high yields of storable food, an animal to carry loads and pull carts or ploughs, and a plant or animal source of fibres. The principal plants available are the cereals, the soya bean, and the potato, and these are of very unequal value for biochemical reasons. For example, maize, as compared with wheat or oats, is very poor in vitamin B2. Hence populations living mainly on maize get a skin disease called pellagra. This is probably one reason why the maize-civilizations of central America never reached the level of the wheat, barley, and rice civilizations of the old world. The other reason is that America was very poor in domesticable animals. The buffalo is no substitute for the cow, and the llama a very poor one for the horse and sheep.

Hence if it is possible to determine where cereals and cattle were first domesticated, we shall have gone a long way towards tracing civilization to its source. This task is being undertaken by Vavilov and other Russian scientists. Karl Marx's *Kapital* has largely replaced the Bible in Russia to-day, and one of Marx's doctrines is that if we know how production is organized in a society we know the most important thing about it, and can even deduce its religious or philosophical system to a large extent. So Russian biologists are studying not only the domesticated animals and plants of to-day, but their ancestors which were the means of production in primitive societies. In the case of wheat the results are fairly clear. There are two distinct groups of wheat, which can only be hybridized with difficulty, and each can be traced to a definite centre. As that centre is approached, more and more different kinds of wheat are found, and these show all kinds of characters, such

as purple shoots, which have been lost in the most
cultivated varieties, and which are shown by breeding
tests to be almost certainly primitive characters. One
of these centres is in Abyssinia, the other, from which
the more important group of wheats is derived, in or
near south-eastern Afghanistan. The former is taken to
be the original home of the agriculture that led up to
Egyptian civilization, the latter the source of Indian
and Mesopotamian wheats, and of the more important
varieties grown in Europe and North America to-day.
What is more, a great many other cultivated plants
seem to have originated in one or the other of these
centres. For example, rye, carrots, turnips, and some
types of beans, lentils, flax, and cotton, seem to be of
Afghan origin. At present the archaeology of these
regions is quite untouched, but the results of excavation, especially in the Afghan area, are likely to be of
extreme interest. Agriculture, if Vaviloff is right, started
in mountains, and only later spread to river valleys.

In the same way a knowledge of the origin of the
dog would throw an immense amount of light on prehistory. Dogs have been domesticated since neolithic
times at least, probably for far longer than cattle, which
is doubtless one reason why they fit better into human
society. However, no one has yet any serious idea where
they were first domesticated.

But to return to better ascertained facts. Between
about 3000 B.C. and A.D. 1400 there was very little
improvement in the quality of civilization at its best.
Yet it did spread out from its original centres in the
valleys of the Nile, Euphrates, and Indus, to cover
an ever wider area. This area sometimes contracted,
as when our ancestors overran the western Roman

Empire, when the Turks destroyed the civilization of Mesopotamia after a continuous run of over 4000 years, or when large areas of Central Asia dried up into deserts. It is probable that an important part in shifting the centres of civilization to more temperate countries was played by the malaria parasite and the hookworm Ankylostoma, which causes anaemia. These can only flourish in warm damp countries, and there is a certain amount of evidence that they have been spread about the world during the last 4000 years.

Between 3000 B.C. and A.D. 1400 there were probably only four really important inventions, namely the general use of iron, paved roads, voting, and religious intolerance. Perhaps I should have added coinage and long-distance water supply. Gunpowder had been known for a long time before A.D. 1400 in China, but did not begin to win battles in Europe till the seventeenth century. Somewhat before that date, however, it had helped to accelerate the decay of feudalism by diminishing the military value of castles. Knowledge progressed slowly, and we now know that we have greatly over-estimated the originality of Greek mathematics. Babylonian mathematical astronomy was very highly advanced. Kidinnu, their last great astronomer, who lived about 400 B.C., was a great deal more accurate in the numbers which he used in predicting eclipses and the like than any of his successors until about fifty years ago. His knowledge had, however, been forgotten in the interval, and his calculations were translated just too late to be of any serious value to astronomers. In Assyria the average educated man knew the multiplication table. As King Ashurbanipal put it in his autobiography, 'I recited the complicated multiplications and divisions which are

E

not immediately apparent'. The same level was not reached in England till the late seventeenth century. Pepys was grown up when he learned his multiplication table.

As regards law, the code of King Dungi, who reigned in Ur about 2340 B.C., compares quite favourably with that of King George IV. of England a century ago. King Dungi's subjects kept slaves, though the slaves were allowed private property. They did not, however, hang children for theft. Their wives, unlike those of our great-grandfathers, were allowed private property, and if their husband took a concubine, instead of having no legal remedy at all, like English women up to 1923, they had the right to make their supplanter wash their feet and carry their chair to church, though she had also certain definite rights as against the husband. As the legal code gives a rough reflection of the moral standards of those who framed it, we may suppose that, on the whole, morals have not greatly improved during the course of history.

Christianity and other religions have, of course, on occasion been great weapons in the hands of moral reformers, but they have also been effectively used for the opposite purpose. To take an obvious example, slavery, and what is worse, slave-raiding, still exist in Christian Abyssinia, the latter evil nowhere else. And when Lloyd Garrison opened his anti-slavery campaign in Boston in 1830 he met with such opposition from all religious bodies that he was compelled to start in an infidel hall.

These facts must be weighed against the religious motives which prompted Wilberforce and Clarkson in their campaign against slavery in the British Empire.

The balance is equally even in the case of other moral reforms.

Iron of a sort was known from a very early age, but it was only produced on a very large scale and of a useful type in the second millennium B.C. At the siege of Troy, about 1200 B.C., it was still an expensive novelty. It made a somewhat higher material level of civilization possible, but it also made war more efficient and terrible. Paved roads increased the possible size of the state, and voting made various republican forms of government possible, though democracy was extremely rare. The so-called democracies of the ancient world were almost invariably governments by associations of slave-owners. Religious intolerance (which was possibly invented by the Jews, and independently by the Zoroastrian Persians) had important effects in producing uniformity of culture, and was a great means of spreading civilization. The ancient Romans, who were not intolerant, could not conquer the Germans, and did not try to make them substitute Jupiter for Thor. Indeed they thought the two were the same. (I always have to remember this fact before I translate 'Jeudi' into English, my natural tendency being to equate Jove with Woden.) St. Boniface and other missionaries persuaded many of the Germans to leave Thor for Christ, and incidentally to adopt various Roman customs which went along with Christianity, just as modern missionaries diffuse trousers and football along with the gospel. In this way the Germans were ultimately civilized. But religious intolerance, both Christian and Mohammedan, also played a great part in lowering the level of civilization throughout what had been the Roman Empire.

Up till about A.D. 1400, then, civilization spread a

great deal, but rose very little. It is only if we confine our attention to such areas as Western Europe, where it arrived very late, that it appears to have improved. In the fifteenth century a new process began. For thousands of years educated people had despised manual labour. This was natural enough when it was largely performed by slaves. But in the late Middle Ages things were different for three reasons. In the first place, the ruling military class were illiterate. Many kings could not sign their names. There was, however, a fair amount of education in other parts of the population. Secondly, thanks to St. Benedict and certain other founders of religious orders, a large number of the clerical class, who were relatively educated, had a first-hand acquaintance with manual labour. Thirdly, the towns were very largely governed by the gilds, in which men who had become skilled workers rose to positions of wealth and power.

Hence the possibilities for experimental investigation on a large scale by educated men arose. The scientists of the past had investigated nature, but almost always by observation and not experiment, and they had never made elaborate apparatus. Plato had believed that the future of humanity lay in the hands of the philosopher who was also a king. He was wrong. The combination required was that of philosopher and craftsman. Modern physics began in Leyden, where the great Simon Stevinus founded statics in 1586 by a study of the principles underlying the lever and the sluice. Incidentally he invented decimals and influenced world history about as much as Napoleon or Washington by devising the system of defence of Holland by sluices. This enabled the Dutch to win the eighty years' war against the Spaniards, who were far better soldiers, and saved the Reformation. And modern industry began with printing about 1450. This invention was important not only because it cheapened books, but because it was the first example of mechanical mass production applied to articles formerly produced one by one.

Even so the old civilization might perhaps have been saved. The main principles which have guided scientific research ever since were laid down by Galileo, who first used the experimental method not merely as an occasional resort in difficult cases, but as a normal method of investigation. The man who is probably the greatest living experimentalist once said to me that but for Galileo and men like him he would never have thought of using experiment rather than unaided observation and thought to search out the nature of things. If Galileo and a few more like-minded men had been burned alive at an early age we might very possibly still be living under a civilization not greatly different from that of the Middle Ages.

But the progress of science was slow. Galileo died in 1642, and it was not till 161 years later that Symington's steam tug, *Charlotte Dundas*, towed two barges for 19½ miles on the Forth and Clyde Canal. Leuwenhoek invented the first efficient microscope in about 1660, and it was two centuries before Pasteur used it to discover the cause of infectious diseases. It is only in the last hundred years that civilization, after six thousand years, has begun to change all through. But to-day the external conditions of life in civilized communities differ more from those of 1829 than did the conditions of 1829 from those at the time of Noah's flood. And this change, the real world revolution, has only just begun. We have gone an immense way in improving and organizing production and communication; we have nearly abolished waterborne and insect-borne diseases, and that is about all. Science has not yet been applied to most human activities. It can be, and I hope will be, applied to all.

The world is, of course, full of alleged applications of science outside the realms of production and hygiene, but the vast majority of them show no trace of scientific method. Thus there are numberless systems of education which are supposed to be based on scientific child psychology. But they are usually applied to small groups of children, in many cases to the children of unusually intelligent parents, brought up in unusually intelligent homes. If such children later turn out to be more successful than the average, this proves nothing at all. In order to prove the superiority of some new system, for example the Dalton plan, it will be necessary to follow up some thousands of average children educated under it, and some thousands educated on the ordinary system, and to find out which group on the average grow up into better citizens. This has not yet been done, and until it has been done it is ridiculous to talk about scientific method in education. Scientific method combines observation with experiment. Experiment without observation may be an enthralling occupation, but it is not science.

But the application of science to industry and medicine has entirely altered political problems. Until a few years ago every 'civilized' country really consisted of a small number of more or less civilized people among a multitude of uneducated poor who shared to a very slight extent in the benefits of civilization. Any equalization of incomes would merely have reduced the few to the level of the many, and destroyed what little culture existed. Socialism and civilization were obviously incompatible. To-day the national income is large enough to admit of universal education, and it could be more evenly divided than it is at present without endangering science, art, or literature. That particular argument against Socialism is no longer valid. And hygiene has provided another serious argument against our present economic system. We now live so long that a large proportion of the capital in many countries is in the hands of people over sixty years of age, who naturally show less enterprise than younger men and women. A good deal of Socialism arises from irritation at this fact, though anti-Socialists can fairly reply that a Government official at forty commonly shows as little enterprise as an ordinary man at sixty-five.

For this reason history helps us very little in deciding for or against Socialism. The situation of to-day is something entirely new. The old civilization, which had lasted for six thousand years, is in process of replacement by something which will differ from it as completely as it differed from savagery. History, as generally taught in schools, is the story of the political squabbles of the last two thousand years, and is, on the whole, rather a futile story. It becomes valuable when it is studied in detail, because it illustrates the psychology of politicians and that of crowds. Far more light is thrown on the English civil war by the fact that Charles I. was afflicted with severe stammering in his youth than by the quaint legal arguments which he used to justify his ill-considered actions. This is why men and women to-day prefer to read biographies of historical characters rather than histories of the British Constitution. We have our Charles I.'s in politics to-day, and biographical history enables us to understand and pity them. But conventional history may lead us to share their delusion that they are now living in the eighteenth century, as Charles I. apparently supposed that he was living in the Middle Ages.

The interpretation of history has tended to oscillate between two fallacies. The obvious fallacy is to regard it as the story of great men and great movements. But on a long view these very nearly cancel one another out. The struggle between freedom and authority has gone on all through history, and any unbiassed person must recognize that both parties at any moment have had a good deal of right on their side. And few of us can be whole-hearted partisans in any war of more than a hundred years past. In disgust with these great political figures we turn to the idealists who took no direct part in government, but produced novel ideas and points of view. Here, we like to think, are the real leaders of mankind.

We are the music-makers, and we are the dreamers of dreams,
Wandering by lone sea-breakers, and sitting by desolate
  streams,
World-losers and world-forsakers, on whom the pale moon
  gleams,
But we are the movers and shakers of the world forever, it
  seems.

We in the ages lying in the buried past of the earth
Built Nineveh with our sighing, and Babel itself with our
  mirth,
And o'erthrew them with prophesying to the old of the new
  world's worth,
For each age is a dream that is dying, or one that is coming
  to birth.

I believe that this is as great a fallacy as the other. The dreamer of dreams can at most replace one set of symbolic ideas by another, the cross by the crescent, or the mother of the gods by the mother of God. After wars and revolutions, crusades and martyrdoms, the new dream is sometimes adopted. The world has been shaken, but there is very little evidence that it has been moved. But if the dreamers and the music-makers have not greatly altered the world by imposing their special dreams on it, the greatest of them have slightly raised the level of human life. We can meet the prospect of death with greater equanimity because Shakespeare wrote—

> Men must endure
> Their going hence, even as their coming hither.
> Ripeness is all.

We can love more passionately because Marvell told his coy mistress that—

> The grave's a fine and private place,
> But none, I think, do there embrace.

And we can be better citizens of the universe, better botanists, even better horticulturists, because Jesus said, 'Consider the lilies how they grow; they toil not, they spin not, and yet I say unto you, that Solomon in all his glory was not arrayed like one of these'.

The reason for the relatively small ultimate effect of the dreamer is, I think, fairly clear. He or she is primarily concerned with the human spirit. Even to-day the workings of the spirit of man largely elude our intellectual grasp. In other words, psychology is not a science. Spiritual things must therefore be shown, if at all, in symbols, and these symbols are interpreted in different ways by different men, so that Blake could write—

> The vision of Christ which thou dost see
> Is my vision's chiefest enemy.
> Yours is the healer of mankind,
> Mine speaks in parables to the blind.

Thus religion tends inevitably to crystallize into theology, and the letter to choke the spirit.

Ultimately I can see no reason to doubt that psychology will become scientific, with results of incalculable importance. Even to-day the first feeble attempts to introduce scientific method into it are producing a change in human thought and conduct only comparable with those which are generally brought about by a new religion.

Who, then, have been the real world-revolutionaries, the men who have done such deeds that human life after them could never be the same as before? I think that the vast majority of them have been skilled manual workers who thought about their jobs. The very greatest of them are perhaps two men or women whose real names will remain forever unknown, but whom we may call Prometheus and Triptolemus, the inventors of fire and agriculture. Prometheus, who was a Neanderthal man* with great brow ridges and no chin, discovered how to keep a fire going, and how to use it to such advantage that his successors were induced to imitate his practice. Probably some later genius discovered how to kindle a fire by rubbing sticks together, and I like to imagine that it was a woman who first presented her

* Recent excavations in China suggest that the ape-man Sinanthropus possessed fire. Prometheus lived longer ago than I thought.

astonished but delighted husband with a cooked meal. Fire was a very ancient invention, made in the early part of the old Stone Age, but apparently seeds were first systematically sown not so very long before the dawn of history. The immediate result was to make possible a fairly dense and settled population in which civilization was able to develop.

All through the historical period great inventions were made which were so clearly useful that they were bound to spread over the earth. Great intellectual discoveries were also made, but they were often forgotten because they led to no practical result. Thus the ancient Egyptian possessed a primitive kind of algebra. The chief algebraical papyrus known to us, which deals with simple equations, is called ' Directions for obtaining knowledge of all dark things'. But this algebra was forgotten and had to be re-invented, because it was not applied to any useful purpose, whereas the Egyptian methods of surveying have developed into those in use to-day. To-day science is important because it is applied, and it is only the applicable portions of science which are reasonably sure of survival.

Compare the two greatest biologists of last century, Pasteur and Darwin. Pasteur's fundamental ideas are fairly sure of survival, because any nation that disbelieved in them would double its death-rate if it carried that disbelief into practice. But although Darwin's main ideas are accepted by most scientific men, no obvious disasters would follow their rejection.

Both in England and America there are religious bodies which are either anti-Pasteurian or anti-Darwinian. It is perfectly conceivable that during the next century the Roman Catholic Church may gain control of Europe, or the fundamentalists of North America. In either case, Darwinism will be proscribed, and the average man will not be much worse off on that account. But if in the next fifty years Darwin's ideas are applied to produce some great improvements in agriculture, hygiene, or politics, such a proscription will at once become more difficult. A government of consistent Christian Scientists, who refused to take preventive measures of a material kind against the spread of epidemic disease, would be far more dangerous than a government of fundamentalists. Darwin's intellectual achievement may have been as great as Pasteur's, but so far it has only led to a change in fashionable beliefs which may not be permanent, while Pasteur's has affected the whole structure of civilized society, and will probably go on doing so.

If I become Pope, which does not at present seem very probable, I shall at once take all the steps in my power to secure the canonization of Pasteur, who was, of course, a sincere Catholic. And I shall give the official blessing of the Church to some of the theories and practices which he introduced. But I shall point out the really weak points in Darwin's argument, which most defenders of the faith seem to miss completely, and anathematize them as errors.

It is significant that Pasteur was not only a great thinker but a superb technician, a man of immense manual skill who invented a great deal of the complex technique by which substances can be kept free from microbes, and one kind of microbe can be grown without contamination by others. Bacteriological theory is largely the verbalization of this technique. Pasteur clearly thought a great deal with his hands, Darwin rather little.

Many of the more historically important ideas were not at first put into words. They were technical inventions, which were at first handed down by imitation, and only slowly developed a verbal theory. When they did the theory was generally nonsense, but the practice sound. This was obviously the case, for example, until quite recently, with the extraction of metals from their ores. Certain methods worked, but no one knew why, and those who thought they knew were wrong. As the historical importance of production was not realized until recently, we shall never know who discovered iron-smelting, or, what would be more interesting, how he discovered it.

But there is another reason too. The first-rate technician is generally much more interested in his craft than in his personal fame, or even in his life. In order to obtain the necessary conditions to create a masterpiece or perfect a new process he is perfectly willing to lose himself in a glorious anonymity. The architects of many of the world's greatest buildings, like the great inventors, are often unknown, and generally mere names. The knowledge that this would be so would not have distressed them. Their attitude is summed up in one of the songs sung by airmen during the war.

> Take the cylinder out of my kidneys,
> The connecting rod out of my brain,
> The camshaft from under my backbone,
> And assemble the engine again.

The engine remains as their very real memorial. Similarly I am inclined to think that such men have been very largely responsible for so much of steady progress as is traceable behind the ebb and flow of history. The British Empire was made possible by the gradual improvement in navigation during the seventeenth and eighteenth centuries, and was consolidated by the steamship. The United States were united by railroads. The aeroplane is going to create the World State.

The point of view which I am urging is unpopular for two reasons, apart from the inevitable shortness of historical views until recently. In the first place, history is written by people impressed with the importance of their own political and religious views, and inevitably takes on the character of propaganda for them. But a more fundamental cause is as follows. Historians have inevitably thought in terms of words. They have read many books and documents. They have often been great stylists like Gibbon and Macaulay. They have realized the power of words to move multitudes. They have not been manual workers, and have seldom realized that man's hands are as important as and more specifically human than his mouth. Those intellectuals who have also been intelligent with their hands have mostly confined their writing to scientific and technical questions. Perhaps I ought to do so myself. But when I look at history, I see it as man's attempt to solve the practical problem of living. The men who did most to solve it were not those who thought about it, or talked about it, or impressed their contemporaries, but those who silently and efficiently got on with their work.

PREHISTORY IN THE LIGHT OF GENETICS*

OUR knowledge of the human past before the dawn of history will probably always be based in the main on the results of actual excavation of artefacts and skeletons. Nevertheless, a study of current phenomena or those of the more recent past may furnish important evidence. Thus, we cannot neglect the evidence from comparative philology which so impressed our grandparents, or that from the geographical distribution of customs which is brought forward by the diffusionist school to-day. I propose to bring to your notice a new class of evidence, that from genetics. Genetics is the branch of biology which deals with the causation of innate differences between organisms. It includes the study of heredity, but has a wider scope, because it explains not only why children resemble their parents, but why they differ from one another. The key to genetics is the discovery by Mendel that the basis of heredity is atomic, the innate constitution of an organism being determined by genes, of which the number is finite. Moreover, any individual (at least in the higher animals) contains either two, one, or none of each kind of gene.

Now the physical characters on which the anthropologist has so far relied are not simple from the genetical point of view. Thus stature, skull shape, and

---

* A discourse delivered at the Royal Institution on Friday, February 20, 1931.

skin colour are modifiable by the environment, and the difference between the hair form of a Bushman and a European depends on several different genes. Moreover, some characters have a considerable selective value, so that we cannot determine the proportions of pure races which have gone to make a mixed people from its present composition. Quite recently, however, a group of characters has been found which is not open to these objections. I refer to the human blood groups.

These were discovered early in the present century in connection with blood transfusion. Every human being belongs to one of four groups. There are sub-groups also, which need not concern us for the moment. The success or otherwise of a transfusion depends on the groups to which the donor and recipient belong. The corpuscles may contain one, both, or neither of two substances called isoagglutinogens A and B. If your corpuscles do not contain A your serum will agglutinate injected corpuscles containing it. They will become sticky, clump together, and finally break up, causing serious illness or death. The results are summarized in Table I, where + represents agglutination of the corpuscles of the donor by the serum of the recipient.

TABLE I

SERUM

Corpuscles.	AB	A	B	O
AB . . .	−	+	+	+
A . . .	−	−	+	+
B . . .	−	+	−	+
O . . .	−	−	−	−

Not only man but other primates, though probably not mammals in general, all belong to one of the four groups AB, A, B, and O. Membership is determined by three genes, A, B, and R, of which any one has two and only two. If you have A and B you belong to group AB. If you have two A's, or A and R, you belong to group A. Similarly, group B members have two B's or B and R, while group O possesses two R's. A parent hands on one of his two genes to each child. This is done at random. Hence the laws of heredity are fairly simple. Group O breeds true. A by A, and A by R, cannot give AB or B. AB by O gives equal numbers of A and B. And so on. No case has been observed of transformation of a member of one group into a member of another.

The facts of Table I. were discovered by Landsteiner and Janssky, the mode of inheritance was only cleared up in 1924 by Bernstein. But during the war two Polish doctors called Hirzfeld, attached to the Serbian army at Salonika, made the surprising discovery that the proportions of the different groups were entirely different in different races. A drop of blood added to two test sera will establish group membership, and the Hirzfelds tested at least 500 bloods of each of fifteen different racial groups, including Africans and Indians as well as Europeans, and Jews as well as Greeks and Turks from Salonika who had lived for many generations in the same environment with little intermarriage. As examples of the results found in such a case, Table II. shows the percentage of the four groups among the races of Hungary.

With the aid of genetics we can carry the analysis a good deal further. Suppose we have three populations, one belonging entirely to group O, one to group A, and

F

TABLE II

Population.	Percentages belonging to groups.			
	AB	A	B	O
Germans in Heidelberg .	5	43	12	40
Germans ⎫	3	43	13	41
Magyars ⎬ in Hungary .	12	39	19	31
Gipsies ⎭	6	21	39	34
Indians in Northern India .	9	19	41	31

one to group B, and each breeding true for the character, *i.e.* homozygous. [It may be remarked in passing that you cannot have a population consisting of group AB only. Membership of this group is a characteristic depending on hybridity, like tortoise-shell colour in cats or steel in rabbits.] So long as our three populations do not mix we shall not get any members of group AB. But even one generation of random mating gives a certain relationship between the percentages of the different groups, which continues to hold even if the population later breaks up into endogamous groups. The figures obtained thus tell us whether a given set of blood samples has been derived from a well-mixed population, or one in which different racial groups have not intermarried. To take two examples, a group of 11,000 bloods from Polish peasants (Jews, Germans, and so on being excluded) indicated mixture, while a group of 1600 bloods from a general hospital in Liverpool showed evidence of several endogamous groups, which are, of course, known to exist there.

Where the population has come into equilibrium through random mating we can estimate the proportions of the three genes, A, B, and R, accurately. Otherwise this can be done approximately. Generally R is the commonest, and fairly often B is the rarest. The proportions are constant in a given race, and are not affected by changed environment in the course of a few centuries. Thus at Salonika there have been endogamous Greek, Turkish, and Jewish communities since the late fifteenth century. The Greek proportions are typically Balkan. The Jews are much the same as Arabs. The Turks are decidedly Asiatic. In Hungary (Table II.), Magyars, Germans, and gipsies have formed approximately endogamous groups for several centuries. The proportions among the Germans are much the same as among those in Germany. The gipsies have ratios similar to Northern Indians, and the Magyars are unlike any other race, though fairly similar to the Japanese.

Clearly, then, we may take the proportions of the blood group genes in any population as indicating racial origin rather than effects of climate or other environmental influences. Hence, if we map the world we shall expect to get information of racial origins quite different to that given by such a character as skin colour. For it is at least highly plausible that the black skin colour of so many tropical peoples is adaptive, light skin being disadvantageous where the sunlight is strong, and conversely.

Fig. I is a map of the world showing the percentages of the gene B among various populations. The unbracketed figures for America and Australia refer to the so-called native populations, i.e. those who had migrated there before the Europeans. The contour lines are drawn at 10, 20, and 30 per cent. The result is perfectly clear. Only in the Punjab does this gene occur in more than 30 per cent. of the population. But as Tibet, Afghanistan, and Persia are blanks, the area of maximum frequency of this gene may extend into one or more of these countries. The area of over 20 per cent. extends to the Pacific on each side of the block formed by China, and into Europe through Ukraine. There is

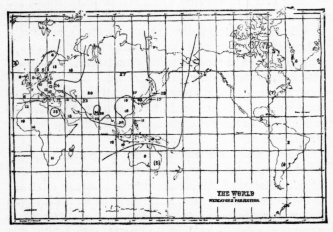

FIG. 1.—Percentage frequency of blood-group gene B in human populations.

a small 25 per cent. island in Egypt, but this is based on a single research only involving 423 people, and which should therefore be accepted with reserve. The island in Scotland is also based on a rather small group. The area of 10 per cent. and over includes the whole of Asia, with Russia and the Balkans, probably covers most of Africa, and extends into Europe as far as Austria. At one time it was thought that the English had less of the gene B than any other people. This is true as compared with any other of the races which are to-day politically important. However, the Australian aborigines certainly, and the Red Indians of North America probably, do not contain this gene at all, the rare cases found being due to recent race mixture.

Although the evidence is clearly incomplete, there is a very strong suggestion that the distribution of the gene B corresponds to a migration outwards from Central Asia in prehistoric times, a migration which did not reach America or Australia, and of which few members reached Western Europe. Superimposed on this our map shows the effects of the well-known migrations into Europe in historic times. There may be another B centre in Northern Africa.*

A corresponding map can be made for the gene A, but it does not give such clear results. It is found almost everywhere, including Australia, but is rare in North America. In Eurasia its frequency seems to increase as we go north. There is a maximum in Lapland, and another among the Ainos of North Japan. Either it has originated in several centres, or else it originated far earlier than B.

Quite recently two new facts have been discovered.

* Since the above was written, one peculiar fact has been discovered by an enterprising Jesuit. The natives of Tierra del Fuego (lying at the southern end of South America) and certain islands off the Chilian coast, carry the gene B in considerable quantities. It is too early to say whether this is due to immigration from Polynesia, or whether they are remnants of a population older than the general mass of Amerindians. I have made no attempt to bring the map up to date for a simple reason. No copies of the *Zeitschrift für Rassenphysiologie*, which deals largely with the questions here discussed, is to be found in London, the capital of the Empire containing the greatest diversity of races. One copy passes through a London bookseller to Australia.

There are two forms of the gene A, one giving a stronger reaction than the other. This may account for the rather irregular distribution of the gene A, with its three maxima, in Lapland, Japan, and Australia. We shall want a world map showing the distribution of the two modifications of A. And there is another pair of allelomorphic genes M and N, determining somewhat more complicated blood reactions. The geographical distribution of these has not yet been studied, but they are known to be present in different proportions among white and coloured New Yorkers, the proportions in Berlin being nearly the same as those among the white population of New York. Here, too, valuable information will doubtless be obtained.

I should like to call the attention of anthropologists to the importance of these studies, especially in connection with primitive and isolated peoples. Apparently a little tact and psychology may work wonders. Thus, the Arunta tribe of Central Australia, who classify themselves into eight exogamous groups, at once appreciated the notion of classifying men on the basis of their bloods, and when one of the eight investigators was appointed a member of each exogamous group, they felt that at last white men were interesting themselves in the realities of life. The general result of blood group studies, then, is to point to a migration in all directions from Central Asia into a more primitive population.

I must now turn to quite a different branch of genetics, that of cultivated plants. To the biologist human society appears not merely as an association of men, but, in its developed stages, as a symbiosis of man with certain animals and plants. These latter are more variable than man, and unlike him, can be bred experimentally. They therefore offer specially hopeful fields for the geneticist.

The work which I am going to describe is that of Vavilov and his colleagues. Vavilov is the head of the U.S.S.R. department of applied botany and plant-breeding. Under the influence of the Marxian philosophy Russian biological research has been concentrated on the investigation of economically important animals and plants, but from a very wide point of view, and on a scale unparalleled elsewhere. For example, I understand that Professor Percival's wheat collection at Reading consists of about 3000 living varieties, Vavilov's at Dyetskoë Syelo of 23,500 when last counted. These are all grown on from time to time, since only by growing varieties side by side can the effects of environment be discounted. In addition, Vavilov's work is based on expeditions to Abyssinia, Afghanistan, Central and South America, and elsewhere. His results, with full English summaries, are given in the Russian 'Bulletin of Applied Botany and Plant-breeding', and also in the report of the International Genetical Congress at Berlin.

De Candolle and others had supposed that cultivated species originated where the most similar wild form is found. As we shall see, this is not true for some crops, such as rye. And it is sometimes untrue for wheat. Thus, he thought wheat had originated in or near Syria, the home of wild emmer. It is true that some wheats cross freely with emmer. But others give sterile hybrids with it, and have therefore probably originated in a different way.

Vavilov's method of determining the place of origin of a cultivated plant takes account of wild species. But it is also based on the idea of centres of diversity. Willis, in his book, *Age and Area*, points out that, if we compare wild species with similar means of dispersal, the oldest have the wider distribution, and the longer a group has been established in a given area, the more species are found there. Thus, the centre of diversity gives a clue to the centre of origin. This is clearly true to some extent for cultivated plants. Thus wheat is an Old-World crop, and many more types are found in the Old World than in America, while the opposite is true for maize.

I shall describe Vavilov's results on wheat and rye in some detail, as they are the most thoroughly worked out of crop plants. The fourteen wheat species (two wild) fall into three groups according to the number of chromosomes in the nucleus. The most primitive form has seven pairs of chromosomes. Other series have fourteen and twenty-one pairs. Hybrids between plants of different chromosome number are more or less sterile, because the chromosomes will not pair, and hence an irregular complement goes into the pollen grain or ovule.

The fourteen-chromosome wheats include the grass *Triticum aegilopoides*, distributed in mountains from the Balkans to the Crimea and Kurdistan. Its domesticated derivative *T. monococcum*, or small spelt, is grown mainly for fodder in isolated mountainous districts from Spain to the Caucasus. It was one of the chief wheats of the Neolithic period in Europe, but survived into the Bronze Age at Troy and in Hungary. It has not been found in Egypt or India. The present cultivation is a relic of the past.

The twenty-eight-chromosome wheats have a wild prototype, the Syrian wild emmer. Cultivated emmer is the main cereal found in Neolithic Europe. It was grown by the Badarians of pre-dynastic Egypt, throughout the dynastic period, and in ancient Mesopotamia. It was the ζεία or *far* of the Greeks and Romans. To-day it is grown mainly for fodder in a few isolated areas, particularly by the Basques in the Caucasus, and by Armenian settlers in Persia. The most important twenty-eight-chromosome wheat is the macaroni wheat, *T. durum*, grown over the Mediterranean region and parts of Central Asia and India. Rivet and so-called Polish wheat have a similar distribution. The centre of diversity in these forms is in the Mediterranean region, particularly North-Eastern Africa, and in Abyssinia.* These wheats are not known for certainty in prehistoric times, but certainly occurred in Graeco-Roman Egypt, and probably as early as the 12th dynasty. They appear therefore to have originated within historic times in the Mediterranean basin, probably from emmer.

The forty-two-chromosome wheats include bread wheat, *T. vulgare*, club wheat, *T. compactum*, and Indian dwarf wheat, *T. sphaerococcum*, along with spelt, *T. spelta*, which has a very restricted distribution. A cytological study of hybrids makes it highly probable that they contain one set of fourteen chromosomes from the genus *Aegilops*, and originated from a cross between a grass of this genus and one of the earlier types of wheat. These wheats have a distribution shown in Fig. 2. The areas overlap in the Punjab and neighbouring hill country, and it is here that the centre of diversity of bread wheat is found. Vavilov lists 15-20 varieties in Europe, 52 in Persia, 60 in Afghanistan. Wheats of this type possibly occurred in Neolithic Europe, but did not become common until the Bronze Age.

* Later work accentuates the importance of Abyssinia.

There can, I think, be little doubt of the poly-phyletic origin of the wheats. The small spelt and

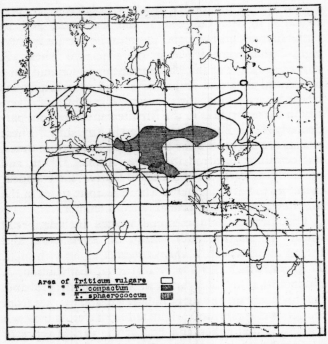

FIG. 2.—Distribution of the main species of wheat with forty-two chromosomes. Very recently planted areas, such as America, South Africa, and Australia, are omitted.

emmer of Neolithic times were gradually replaced by macaroni and rivet wheat from a centre in or near Egypt, and bread wheat from a centre near the Punjab.

The history of rye is quite different. It is mainly cultivated in regions too cold for wheat, such as northern Europe, and the mountainous parts of Afghanistan. But it is common as a weed in wheat crops, and primitive peoples sow mixed crops, the proportion of rye rising from 3 per cent. to 39 per cent. at successive heights in Turkestan, until at great heights pure rye is grown. Replacement in a mixed crop brought into new surroundings is very rapid, and it would seem that rye replaced wheat automatically as its users migrated northwards or upwards. In just the same way oats appeared as a weed in emmer. Oats and rye are thus secondary crops, as compared to primary crops such as wheat and barley. It is interesting to speculate on the effects upon primitive man of a change in his crop-plant due either to migration or a deterioration of the climate. Although all barleys have the same chromosome number they fall into two groups whose hybrids are partly sterile. One group is centred in North-Eastern Africa, the other in South-Eastern Asia. Millet is centred in Mongolia, and appears to have been largely spread by nomads.

On such lines Vavilov distinguishes six main centres of origin of crop plants (Fig. 3). Area 1, of which the most important section is perhaps the fold between the Hindu Kush and the Himalayas, was the original home of the bread wheats, the small-seeded types of flax and leguminous plants, Old-World cottons, the turnip, carrot, apricot, and peach.

Area 2, in South-Eastern Asia, gave us the hull-less barley, the millet, the soy-bean, and many fruit-trees.

Area 3, round the Mediterranean, produced the hard

wheats, the large-seeded flax and leguminous plants, the beet, the olive, and the fig.

Area 4, in Abyssinia, was the origin of ordinary barleys, probably emmer, and certain beans and forage plants.

Area 5, in Central and South America, produced maize, the potato, tobacco, New-World cottons, and other important plants.

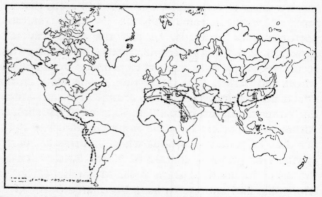

FIG. 3.—Centres of origin of cultivated plants according to Vavilov. Explanation in text.

Possibly a sixth area in the Philippines was the original home of rice.

In almost every case it would appear that crop plants originated in mountainous countries. If this is correct, the great agricultural civilizations of the Nile, Euphrates, and Indus valleys were secondary; and although the first social organization permitting large-scale irrigation and towns probably originated in one of them, we must go further back in time, and higher up in space, to find the first agricultural civilization.

The above summary is, of course, very inadequate. In particular, I have said nothing as to the genetical analysis of the plants from the centres of origin, which often contain many genes dominant to those found in the cultivated varieties. Thus many of the Afghan peas have purple stems, dark seed-coats, and ribbed leaflets. The factors determining these characters have been lost in the course of cultivation.

While the work here described is far from complete, I think that it has now progressed so far that no anthropologist who wishes to take a large view of human origins can possibly neglect it.

POSSIBILITIES OF HUMAN
EVOLUTION

THE majority of educated Englishmen now believe that they are descended from lower animals, though very few of them, under cross-examination, could give valid reasons for their belief, unless indeed they had just been reading Wells, Huxley, and Wells' *Outline of Biology*. If this belief is true, it follows that our descendants may be creatures as different from ourselves as we are different from apes. The probable nature of such a further evolution, if any, is an amusing theme for speculation, but our views on it must depend on our theories as to human evolution in the past. Among those who have recently written on human evolution are our leading humourists, Shaw and Chesterton. Unfortunately they did not confine themselves to being funny about it. Both Chesterton in *The Everlasting Man* and Shaw in *Back to Methuselah* gave what purport to be serious views on evolution. Chesterton is the more easily dealt with. He is greatly impressed by the fact that some prehistoric men drew pictures, and points out that they were presumably quite human from the psychological point of view, and quite different from animals. Now the earliest known art is of the Aurignacian period, probably not more than 50,000 years ago. The men who made it were anatomically human, and their skeletons had no ape-like characters. But worked flints and more or less human skeletons go back enormously further into the past. The Piltdown man lived somewhere round half a million years ago, and the flints from the East Anglian crag, which appear to be human products, are far older. Unless Mr. Chesterton is going to regard these old flint-makers as intelligent pre-Adamite apes, he should admit that only for the last tenth or so of his career have we any evidence that man was an artist. That period is so short from a geological point of view, that the skeletons not only of man, but of most other animals, have hardly undergone any visible change during it. If anything our average brain size has diminished. Mr. Chesterton has some claims to be our greatest living low-brow poet since Kipling has ceased to write verse. As I find it hard to suppose that our immediate posterity will mostly be high-brows, it is likely that his poetry will be read for some time after his death. Should I survive him I shall be one of his readers. But the mere progress of education is likely to thin out the ranks of the readers of his non-fictional prose. May I take this opportunity to beg him to confine himself, in the future, so far as possible to Father Brown (whose chronicles even grace the railway bookstalls of Moscow) and poetry.

Mr. Shaw is a slightly harder nut to crack. A biologist can read the whole of *Back to Methuselah* with amusement and occasional delight. But the author gives himself away in the preface. If he had written *Macbeth* (and I can pay him no greater compliment than to suggest the possibility), the preface would have been a treatise on the danger which witchcraft still presented to Britain. If he had written *The Winter's Tale*, in which Perdita is marooned on the desert coasts of Bohemia, he would have explained how the Czechoslovaks, hemmed in between the sea and the trackless waste, developed the ferocity which had enabled them to subjugate so many neighbouring nations. Shakespeare did not, one supposes, take either witchcraft or the Bohemian coast very seriously. Shaw, however, believes in Lamarckism, a doctrine supported by far less positive evidence than exists for the reality of witchcraft. The reason for this support is fairly clear. Samuel Butler was a better stylist and a more amusing writer than Charles Darwin. Shaw is therefore willing to take his word against Darwin's. Unfortunately, however, Darwin had a greater respect for facts than Butler. Moreover, Shaw finds the idea of evolution by natural selection quite horrid, though he is honest enough to admit that it cannot be disproved.

But he likes to think that if we want a thing hard enough, we or our descendants will get it. Like the Devil (whom, according to some of my correspondents, I resemble in several particulars) I can quote Scripture, and my favourite quotation for Lamarckians is 'Which of you, by taking thought, can add one cubit unto his stature?' For this would be an easier feat than adding two hundred years to one's life, like Mr. Barnabas. Several men are known to have measured nine feet, none to have lived three hundred years. Moreover, when animals or plants are induced to alter their structure by putting them in a new environment, such changes are not handed on to their children. Actually Shaw's knowledge of vital statistics is on a par with Shakespeare's of Bohemian geography. In *The Intelligent Woman's Guide to Socialism and Capitalism*, that interesting repository of nineteenth-century Socialist theory, he says that, thanks to Government regulations, the lungs of Sheffield steel-grinders, which used to be very unhealthy, are now as good as those of the average man. In 1921–1922, the date of the last available statistics, the death-rates of grinders in the cutlery trade from consumption and bronchitis, their two worst lung diseases, were each between seven and eight times that of the general population. A similar lack of contact with mere facts characterizes Shaw's somewhat bizarre opinions on medical research and science generally.

What would a biologist, given the necessary financial resources, actually do to create a race of long-lived beings such as Shaw has so brilliantly imagined? He would not rely on wishing. A doctor in one of Anatole France's novels has dealt well and truly with the influence of parental wishes. 'I often see children with strawberry marks', he says, 'whose mothers say that they desired strawberries before their birth. I am waiting to see a baby marked with a pearl necklace.' Our biologist would go to the actual long-livers. At any moment in the world there are generally two or three men over a hundred and twenty years of age. One has recently left Constantinople for the United States, and another is said to be alive in the Caucasus. Old Parr, our last English long-liver, apparently lived from 1483 to 1635. These men are not in the least like the ordinary old man. They are generally capable of intense physical exertion during their second century. Old Parr did public penance in church for begetting a bastard at a hundred and one. The Caucasian Methuselah was, till quite recently, in the habit of bathing in glacier streams. They are perhaps representative of a new type of humanity rather than exceptional specimens of the ordinary kind.

Now from time to time new varieties of rabbit appear.

G

One of the latest kinds has short fur, and is at present valuable because it is believed, on rather inadequate grounds, that their skins, without further treatment, will be transformable into coney seal fur coats. When a rabbit of a new type turns up, he or she is mated with a normal one. The progeny are usually normal, but when mated together, some of their young are of the new kind. By the time a long-liver reaches a hundred and twenty, he is generally at least a great-grandfather, often by several different wives. The millionaire human biologist would arrange marriages of convenience with large family allowances, between as many of his grandchildren and great-grandchildren as possible. About one in four of marriages between grandchildren might be expected to give rise to long-livers, since the laws of heredity are the same for man and rabbits. Thus in a few centuries a race of long-lived folk could be built up. I doubt if they would be as intelligent as Shaw's Irishmen of 3000 A.D., but once long life were established as a hereditary character it could probably be combined with intelligency, which is also hereditary, though not always very strongly so.

We do not know enough about the specially long-lived men to be able to say whether, like most of their fellows, they become incapable of learning from experience at an age which may be as low as fifteen, but is hardly ever greater than sixty. Unless they retain their mental flexibility for a greater period than the normal man, they would be a mere nuisance.

Actually length is one of the least important qualities which a human life can have. Jesus did not live long. But his ideas have done so. It is worth considering what inheritable qualities should be aimed at if man is to make the attempt to direct his own evolution in the future. The problem is not likely to be a practical one for a century or so, because we do not know the laws governing the inheritance of any but a few human characteristics, and the most that we could do at present would be to prevent the transmission of a few undesirable traits and to encourage desirable ones in a haphazard way. The immediate problem to-day is to create a social organization in which the majority of men and women as they are can be happy and useful. It is possible at least to imagine a society into which about 98 per cent. of the population of most civilized countries would fit. There are, however, a certain small proportion of born misfits. Most of these suffer from serious physical and mental defects, but there are perhaps a still smaller minority who are not too bad, but too good, for life as it is to-day or could be made within our lifetimes. They are intensely sensitive to evils which most of us bear with little trouble, but which our descendants will perhaps find intolerable, and abolish. Some of these people are cranks, some live an externally normal but inwardly unhappy life. Many, I expect, end in asylums or suicides' graves. They may be representative, as far as sensibility is concerned, of humanity a thousand years hence, who will not, I hope, have to put up with many things that distress us. But it is as unfortunate to be born too soon in man's history as too late.

The great majority of us are quite capable of some kind of useful activity. The essential social problems of to-day, as they present themselves to a biologist, are to determine the abilities of different people, and to organize society so that the demand for various kinds of human ability should equal the supply. To-day these problems are not solved. As an examiner I have to gauge the capacity of students according to a system which is obviously inadequate, but I should find it difficult to devise a better; and the system of selection for scientific careers is vastly better than for most others. As regards demand, the maladjustment is still more obvious. There is an insufficient demand for the lower grades of ability, resulting in widespread unemployment. And at the other end of the scale the demand exceeds the supply. There are not enough men and women available with the ability to run industries organized on a nation-wide or world-wide scale.

Russia is attempting the vast experiment of Socialism. The success or otherwise of this experiment depends largely on the ability of fifteen men who constitute the committee of Gosplan, the state-planning organization which is attempting to industrialize the nation. But the problem before other nations is essentially similar. If our civilization breaks down, it may be because modern industry and transport require organization on so vast a scale that human minds of sufficient reach for the purpose are not available. The problem appears most clearly in connection with the history of revolutions. The Dutch revolution against Spain in the sixteenth century was saved by the great engineer, Simon Stevin, who, as Quartermaster-General of the United Netherlands, organized its defence by flooding. The same thing occurred with the French revolution. Lazare Carnot, who, like Stevin, was a mathematician, organized the supply of munitions to the revolutionary armies. He was the permanent feature of a number of successive governments whose more vociferous members, such as Danton, Robespierre, and St. Just, were guillotined.

When the real history of the Russian revolution is written, which will not be for many years, it may prove that Karpoff's reorganization of the chemical industry in 1919 was as vital a factor in its success as the more showy activities of Trotsky.

The position is just the same in science, literature, and the arts. There is plenty of room at the top. In biology we need men with a knowledge not only of the biological sciences, but of mathematics, physics, chemistry, and sociology. Without such supermen biology will break up into a group of isolated sciences divorced from one another, and from human life. Our needs in literature are essentially similar. The average novel-writer appears to know one or two sections of society only. He or she may produce a series of quite competent stories about farmers, high-brows, criminals, sailors, rich women, or what not. Very few serious attempts, however, are made to portray society as a whole, which it is. And such attempts generally fail because of the immense reach required in a mind which is to do the kind of thing which H. G. Wells has occasionally accomplished.

In many nations there are doubtless huge untapped reserves of talent. But in the United States the rising generation is pretty thoroughly searched for certain kinds of ability, and the supply does not equal the demand. No one can say at present whether the demand is likely to be better met in future. In the next generation it will probably not be met, for at present the stupider sections of society are breeding faster than the more intelligent in most civilized countries. There are, however, some hopeful signs. One is the eugenic movement in so far as it leads its intelligent and healthy adherents to produce large families. Another, at least in Europe, is the movement for family limitation. A generation ago the people who limited their families were people who thought for themselves. The average couple produced a large family. Now the position is reversed in many countries. In England, for example, among the well-to-do, but also to an only slightly less extent among many sections of the working classes, there is a taboo against large families. To have seven or ten children is an eccentricity bordering on bad form. This is no doubt a good thing, as England, at least, is somewhat over-crowded.

And I suspect that its results will ultimately be eugenic. To-day there is mass suggestion in favour of family limitation, as there was mass suggestion against it in the past.

> The man of independent mind
> He looks and laughs at a' that.

So does the woman of independent mind. Such people will do their best to have as many children as they want, whether this number is more or less than that laid down by their neighbours. Among my own acquaintances, those who have families of six and over are, without exception, couples of whom one at least displays originality in other respects. Two of them go so far as to wear beards in middle life. So it may be that as birth control becomes fashionable the result in the future will be an increase in the relative number of children born to intelligent parents, just as in the past it has had the opposite effect.

Any political movements which diminish the importance of inherited wealth are, I think, eugenically desirable. So long as such wealth determines our social status it will continue to have two effects. First it will be an incentive to family limitation amongst those who have anything to leave. And secondly, it will cause members of small families to come into better social positions than people with many brothers and sisters. It was, of course, an Irishman who said that it was hereditary in his family to have no children, but there was some truth in the remark. Heiresses commonly acquire their wealth by being only children, and they often marry able men who have no capital, but have risen socially by their ability. But as infertility is strongly inherited, the result is that their husbands have fewer children than the average, and thus ability is to some extent sterilized.

There is thus at least a sporting chance that in the next century we may stop evolving downhill as rapidly as we seem to be doing at present, but that does not mean that we shall start evolving upwards. There is no evidence that the innate abilities of man have improved in the last 30,000 years, though of course his habits and knowledge have done so to an incredible extent. But the man who discovered the use of fire must have been a man of immense enterprise and intelligence, and would very possibly find out how to make petrol out of chalk, water, and wind power if he were alive to-day.

We cannot expect nature to start improving our innate abilities once more. The usual fate of a species in the past has not been progress, but extermination, very often after deteriorating slowly through long periods. The animals and plants alive to-day are the descendants of the few species which have escaped this fate. There is no reason to suppose that man will escape it unless he

makes an effort to do so. And we do not at present know
how to make that effort. Doubtless complete idiots
should be prevented from breeding, but the effort to
eliminate all sorts of 'unfit' human types is a very much
more dubious proposition. When I hear people talking
of the 'elimination of the unfit', I am always reminded
of the crowd who shouted at St. Paul, 'Away with such
a fellow from the earth, for it is not fit that he should
live'. St. Paul was eliminated, and very possibly would
be to-day. Many of the 'unfit' are unfit for society as it is
to-day, but that is often society's fault. The attempt to
prevent them from breeding really involves the appalling
assumption that society as at present constituted is
perfect, and that our only task is to fit man to it. That is
why eugenists are generally conservative in their political
opinions. It also goes a long way to explain the objection
which many religious people feel for negative eugenics.
They regard it as interference with God's will. I do not
share this view, but still less do I regard the average
medical board or bench of magistrates as qualified to
direct the evolution of the human race. The great
geneticist, William Bateson, expressed himself forcibly
on the qualifications needed for the person who was to
select those human types at which to aim. 'I would trust
Shakespeare', he said, 'but I would not trust a committee of Shakespeares.'

But even Shakespeare would be hard put to it to
direct human breeding to-day. He would have been
able, in a rough way at least, to answer one of the two
great questions which will have to be answered before
mankind can control its own evolution. He could have
told us as well as any other man who has ever lived how
a given human being would behave in given circum-

stances. But he could not have predicted what types would arise from a given union. Where he allowed his characters to discuss genetics, as in the case of Gloucester's two sons in *King Lear*, they often utter elementary fallacies.

Before mankind can seriously attempt to control its own evolution, there must be an enormous development of two sciences which are now in their infancy, namely individual psychology and genetics. Each of them is likely to have a bright future because they share the important quality of modesty. The art of successful scientific research is rather like that of successful cross-examination of witnesses. It consists of asking nature simple questions, one at a time. The individual psychologist does not ask what is the nature of the soul, but how the major differences between the behaviours of Mr. Smith and Mr. Jones may be accounted for. The geneticist limits his problems still further. He is only concerned with innate differences, and small ones at that. He does not ask what is the nature of a dog, and he can as yet tell you very little as to what determines that a given embryo shall develop into a dog rather than a cat. But he can already to some extent answer the question why a baby dachshund does not grow up into a Newfoundland. He can also answer simple questions about man. He can tell you what it is in the negro that determines that his hair can be kinky, or why some men, but not others, are colour-blind.

But he can only answer similar questions as to the grosser kinds of psychological differences, such differences as cannot be affected by changes in the environment. No amount of training will cure certain types of idiocy, and the geneticist can sometimes discover why a

given child was born a hopeless idiot. But environment
counts for a great deal in determining most differences
of behaviour. Here is a habitual criminal whom neither
punishment nor kindness has reformed. The geneticist
is quite as likely to be impressed by his persistence as his
criminality. If he had been exposed to different sugges-
tions at a susceptible age he might perhaps have been
equally indefatigable in virtuous conduct. Clearly the
geneticist cannot tackle the problem of the criminal
until the psychologist has told him whether the innate
difference which distinguishes him from the average
man is one of obstinacy, lack of self-control, or some
third factor. The geneticist can at least be certain that
there is generally an innate difference. There are two
different types of twins, dizygotic twins who differ
nearly as much as ordinary brothers or sisters, and
monozygotics, who have the same innate qualities. In a
group of cases examined by Prof. Lange the odds on a
man being a criminal if his monozygotic twin was
criminal were three to one. But criminality of a dizygotic
twin only led to a probability of one in eight. Clearly the
environments were nearly the same in both cases. It
was the inborn characteristics which mainly determined
whether a man should be a criminal or not in that
particular environment.

Before we can give a satisfactory account of the nature
of human differences an amount of work must be done
compared to which the entire body of science up to the
present date will probably appear insignificant. Merely
as tools in the investigation we shall need in the near
future two new branches of mathematics, one new
branch of biochemistry, and a new technique in microscopy. In order to calculate just what would happen if

some of Darwin's views were correct I find myself compelled to embark upon vector analysis in many-dimensional space, a task for which I am very ill equipped; and no adequate prediction of the probable results of birth control can be made, so far as I can see, without using functions of a complex variable, that is to say, what is vulgarly known as the square root of minus one. It is quite possible that the investigation may never be undertaken. Its results would clearly revolutionize religion, politics, and law, and thus be unwelcome to conservatives. But in all probability they would be quite equally damaging to the various substitutes for these human activities which are being put forward to-day by 'advanced' thinkers. For example, the great political movement in Central Europe whose symbol is the swastika is associated not only with pantheistic views in religion but with certain opinions on human biology. These last have no serious scientific foundation, but are just sufficiently touched with science to make them plausible to those who have had an elementary education in biology. The same is true, though in a lesser degree, of much that goes under the names of eugenics and psychology in the United States. The tendency at work is the craving which most of us feel for certainty, the refusal to accept the fact that certain questions will not be answered within our own lifetimes. A favourite refuge with those who will not face this rather disconcerting fact is the Catholic Church. Dogmatism on human biology is psychologically a half-way house to Rome.

Hence the outlook for an unbiassed investigation of human biology is perhaps darkest just in those countries where the largest number of people take it seriously. In

England the greatest subject of general interest is sport, and such serious work as is being done upon human genetics generally passes unnoticed, largely because its results do not greatly flatter anybody. So far so good, but as a consequence very little research is undertaken. Perhaps it is unlikely that a civilization whose basic ideals resemble those of our own should offer favourable ground for such a research. If so, it will presumably collapse like its predecessors, though with a more resounding crash, and the problem will, one hopes, be taken up by a more biologically minded race.

But if, in some remote and fortunate future age, man succeeds in controlling his own evolution, what may we imagine that he will be like? Before we answer this question it is worth pointing out the most fundamental biological difference between man and the apes and monkeys. Man is a creature of much slower growth than any other warm-blooded animal of his size. The slowing of growth has already begun in apes, which mature much less quickly than, for example, dogs or sheep of the same size. One result of this slowing has been that the apes, and to a still greater extent man, never develop certain characters of their adult ancestors, but preserve those of the young or even unborn stage. For example, a puppy a month before birth has a relatively large brain, and its eyes, if it is placed on all fours, look downwards like a man's instead of upwards. Later on the growth of the puppy's brain slows down, and his face straightens out into a snout. In mice the eyes are still pointing downwards at birth. But in man this embryonic type of head remains. A gorilla is born almost hairless except for its head, and only becomes hairy all over as it grows up. An adult man is like a baby gorilla not only in being mainly hairless, but in having no bony brow-ridges, and in other respects.

Our mental superiority over the animals is perhaps largely due to the fact that we never develop certain characteristics found in most adult animals. Our behaviour is less determined by instinct, that is to say inborn reaction patterns, and we are more teachable. A large proportion of mankind, after a more or less human childhood, become almost unteachable. They are sure of everything. They know what is right in politics, religion, art, and human behaviour. They are the pillars of Church and State. Perhaps they are a social necessity. But they have grown out of a large part of their humanity. And I sometimes feel that it would be more appropriate if they were hairy all over.

Perhaps this evolutionary process of slowing down has gone as far as it can. But it is at least probable that any really progressive evolution in the future would take man further from the ape. If so, we should presumably drop a good many of the characteristics on which we pride ourselves, and which most of us even attribute to the Almighty, who is described as the Ancient of Days, not the Ever-young. Assuming that human evolution continues, I suspect that a man of to-day plunged fifty or a hundred thousand years to the future would say something like this:

'These weak, degenerate, childish creatures never seem to grow up. They are not even adult till thirty, and never reach what I should call maturity at all. Their technical achievements afford them plenty of leisure, which they fritter away in the most shameless manner. Their religions (if you can call ritual almost divorced from belief a religion) are a matter of "Let's pretend" rather than "I believe". Their science, where it is not mere technology, seems to be inspired by idle curiosity about trivial matters rather than a genuine desire for truth on fundamental questions. Their philosophy, so far as I can understand it, is a series of rather bad jokes which enable them to shelve the great problems that divided thinking humanity in my time. If they avoid war and some of the other evils of the past, it is largely because an innate instability makes them incapable of combining for any serious purpose. Such objection as they feel for war is not, as it seems to me, on moral grounds at all, but is due to a morbid hypersensitivity which would utterly unfit them for the real and earnest life of to-day.

'As for sexual morals, as far as I can see, they haven't got any, though they take a good deal of trouble to produce the sort of children they want, and their excessive squeamishness keeps them out of some kinds of mischief. They are healthy enough in the negative sense of not getting ill, but they coddle their bodies and are incapable of great exertion.

'Undoubtedly they are more intelligent than we, but they make a very poor use of their minds. A man will give up a brilliant scientific career to write what I should call nonsense verse, and leave that after a year or two for administration or wood-carving. They seem to me to be a race of smatterers who do not take life seriously. In the course of evolution they have lost quite as much as they have gained.'

No doubt such an opinion would be unjust in many ways. A palaeolithic man placed among ourselves would probably regard higher mathematics as no more serious than cross-words. Many of the activities of our descendants would no doubt be quite unintelligible to us. But for all that, I doubt whether even the most enlightened of us would approve of our descendants, assuming that evolution continues on the same lines as in the past. Fortunately we shall not be there to disapprove.

Mr. Bernard Shaw in *Back to Methuselah* imagined an entirely different sort of evolution. He thinks that the development of the human race thirty thousand years hence will be greatly speeded up, so that they will be born talking; by the age of six they will have got over love, art, and other little weaknesses which for most of us make life worth living. After this they will devote most of their very long lives to pure thought. I hope he is wrong.

Another prophet, Mr. Stapledon, in *Last Men and First Men*, goes many millions of years into the future, and describes a humanity which takes nearly two thousand years to grow up, lives two hundred thousand years, but continues to indulge in love, art, and even sport, when fully adult, although vastly more intelligent than ourselves. He also depicts the failure of an earlier experiment in human evolution, which produced a race with great brains and diminutive bodies, in whom the intellect was developed to the exclusion of the emotions, as in Mr. Shaw's ancients.

Such speculations as these are very far from idle. They are eminently desirable, because man does not generally even know what he wants, much less how to get it. A discussion of possibilities will have two effects. It will enable people to come to some opinions as to the possible goal of human evolution (not the ultimate goal of course, but the furthest limit to which our desires and imaginations reach). And it will focus attention on the necessity for more knowledge before we can even suggest means of attaining that goal.

Pictures of the future are myths, but myths have a very real influence in the present. Modern political ideas are very largely the creation of the Jewish prophets, who foresaw the new Jerusalem in the future, at a time when their contemporaries of other nations had no particular hopes for the betterment of humanity. History has certainly been very different from what Isaiah and Daniel believed it would be; but they helped to make it what it is, and perhaps they would not be altogether dissatisfied with it if they could live to-day. Our greatest living mythologist, Wells, is certainly influencing the history of the future, though probably in ways which he does not suspect.

The time will probably come when men in general accept the future evolution of their species as a probable fact, just as to-day they accept the idea of social and political progress. We cannot say how this idea will affect them. We can be sure that if it is accepted it will have vast effects. It is the business of mythologists to-day to present that idea. They cannot do so without combining creative imagination and biological knowledge.

SCIENCE AND ETHICS *

W E are met here to celebrate the memory of Moncure Daniel Conway. We are united by the fact that we do not adopt a merely negative attitude in the face of the collapse of Christianity. We have a task of salvage—a task in which Conway himself played an important part. But the main function of an Ethical Society should be constructive. If we Rationalists could conserve the Christian virtues while abandoning the equally Christian vices, we should have accomplished much. But we aspire to something more positive, a synthesis of a new ethic; tentative, of course, for we lay claim to guidance by no holy spirit save our own consciences, but yet taking cognizance of facts, both in human nature and in the external world, which Christianity has ignored. Conway's career as a prophet began with his realization of the evil of slavery, which St. Paul had condoned; and in later life he championed views on international and inter-racial relationships which earned him in his own day the title of crank, and in ours that of the forerunner of many ideas which have obtained very wide adhesion, if not, as yet, universal application.

I cannot attribute the honour which this Society has done me to the possession of any such ethical genius, if I may use the expression, as distinguished Conway from his fellows. I take it that I am here because the Society

* Conway Memorial Lecture delivered at Essex Hall, April 18, 1928.

realizes that ethics must take the fullest cognizance of the results of natural science, and that I am one of the relatively rare professional scientists who realize vividly, if inadequately, the importance for ethics of the work which we are doing. I do not suppose that I shall solve any ethical problems to-day. That is not my function. Yet I may be able in some degree to elucidate the nature of certain among them; to place them, as it were, against their proper background, and thus to assist those better qualified than myself in coming to conclusions of ethical value.

Science impinges upon ethics in at least five different ways. In the first place, by its application it creates new ethical situations. Two hundred years ago the news of a famine in China created no duty for Englishmen. They could take no possible action against it. To-day the telegraph and the steam-engine have made such action possible, and it becomes an ethical problem what action, if any, is right. Two hundred years ago a workman generally owned his own tools. Now his tool may be a crane or steam-hammer, and we all have our own views as to whether these should belong to shareholders, the State, or guilds representing the workers.

Secondly, it may create new duties by pointing out previously unexpected consequences of our actions. We are all agreed that we should not run the risk of spreading typhoid by polluting the public water supply. We are probably divided as to the duty of vaccinating our children, and we may not all be of one mind as to whether a person likely to transmit club-foot or cataract to half his or her children should be compelled to abstain from parenthood.

Thirdly, science affects our whole ethical outlook by

influencing our views as to the nature of the world—
in fact, by supplanting mythology. One man may see
men and animals as a great brotherhood of common
ancestry, and thus feel an enlargement of his obligations.
Another will regard even the noblest aspects of human
nature as products of a ruthless struggle for existence,
and thus justify a refusal to assist the weak and suffering.
A third, impressed with the vanity of human efforts
amid the vast indifference of the universe, will take
refuge in a modified epicureanism. In all these attitudes
and in many others there is at least some element of
rightness.

Fourthly, in so far as anthropology is becoming
scientific, it is bound to have a profound effect on
ethics by showing that any given ethical code is only
one of a number practised with equal conviction and
almost equal success; in fact, by creating comparative
ethics. But, of course, any serious study of the habits of
foreigners, whether scientific or not, has this effect, as
comes out plainly enough in the history of ancient
Greek ethics. Hence science is not wholly responsible
for the ethical results of anthropology.

Finally, ethics may be profoundly affected by an
adoption of the scientific point of view; that is to say,
the attitude which men of science, in their professional
capacity, adopt towards the world. This attitude includes a high (perhaps an unduly high) regard for truth,
and a refusal to come to unjustifiable conclusions which
expresses itself on the plane of religion as agnosticism.
And along with this is found a deliberate suppression
of emotion until the last possible moment, on the ground
that emotion is a stumbling-block on the road to truth.
So a rose and a tapeworm must be studied by the same

methods and viewed from the same angle, even if the work is ultimately to lead to the killing of the tape-worms and the propagation of roses. Again, the scientific point of view involves the cultivation of a scientific aesthetic which rejoices in the peculiar forms of beauty which characterize scientific theory. Those who find an intimate relation between the good and the beautiful will realize the importance of the fact that a group of men so influential as scientific workers are pursuing a particular kind of beauty. Finally, since the scientist, as such, is contributing to an intellectual structure that belongs to humanity as a whole, his influence will inevitably fall in favour of ethical principles and practices which transcend the limits of nation, colour, and class.

Personally, I believe that the second of these relationships between science and ethics is that in which science is most beneficial. By complicating life science creates new opportunities of wrong-doing; by altering our world-view it may lead us into one form or another of ethical nihilism: it can never do us harm by pointing out to us the consequences of our actions. But the enemies of science will claim that, just because at present, in so far as it concerns itself with human beings, it deals with their bodies rather than their souls, it will lead us to neglect the higher forms of duty to our neighbour. On the whole, I accept this indictment, and glory in it; although, since I do not believe in a detachable soul, I regard the good of the body as the good of the soul too, each being the whole man looked at from a particular point of view. But I welcome this apparent debasement of ethical aims for another reason.

As long as my services to my neighbour are confined to feeding him when hungry, or helping him to raise his wages, and tending him when sick or preventing future sickness, and so forth, I am probably following the Golden Rule, for I do not want to be hungry, poor, or sick, and few of my neighbours are good enough Christians to do so. But if I soar above the mere claims of the body I shall try to educate my neighbour against his will, convert him to my particular brand of religion or irreligion, or even to psycho-analyse him. As I do not personally want to admire Gertrude Stein, worship a biscuit, or remember the moral lapses of my infancy, these forms of charity are very liable to be breaches of the Golden Rule; and if they are carried too far they may well develop into missions to the heathen or even crusades.

I confess that I am not appalled at the thought of an ethical system in which the only goods with which we attempted to provide our neighbours were of the most material character, and in which hygiene took the place of salvation. So much nonsense is put about in the name of hygiene that the idea is naturally repugnant to many people. For hygiene has furnished a new weapon to the numerous persons who desire either to interfere with the lives of their fellows or to exploit their fears. As religion declines, the man who would have sold relics in the past turns his attention to pills, and the belief in the danger of Sabbath-breaking is replaced by that in the danger of bad smells, although tanners and glue-boilers are healthier than the average of the population.

In view of such facts it requires considerable education to preserve one's health; and since the education in question is biological, and I am a biologist, it is natural that I should like to see it universally diffused. If the great aim of education is to know yourself, it is essential to begin at the beginning—namely, with anatomy and physiology. If an almost equally important aim is to promote human solidarity, it is in the realm of hygiene that this is most completely displayed. On the political and economic plane my neighbours' misfortune may be my advantage; in that of hygiene this is never so, as Carlyle pointed out long ago. As long as we maintain slums and dusty occupations we shall have foci from which the tubercle bacillus can attack the well-to-do. As long as we have families of six in a single room we shall be unable to prevent the spread of diphtheria or measles. This solidarity against pathogenic micro-organisms extends beyond the boundaries of nationality, race, or even species. Every Roumanian infected with infantile paralysis, every Indian with smallpox, every rat with plague, diminishes the probable length of my life. The pessimistic psychologists tells us that men can be combined in large numbers only by hate and fear. As long as a single infectious disease remains in existence there will be suitable objects of hatred and fear for humanity as a whole. I am not a materialist, but I do not think that the influence of materialism on ethics is wholly bad. Not only does it banish many imaginary goods and evils, but it calls attention to a case where egoism and altruism are the same. And a materialistic criterion, such as health, has the immense advantage over a hedonistic one such as happiness that the health of two men can be compared, while their happiness cannot.

To my mind, the greatest danger to which our ethical system is exposed from science is not a debasement of values for such reasons as I have sketched, but the deliberate exploitation of scientific ideas in the interests of unscientific prejudice. I cannot choose a better example than the recent lecture on 'Scientific Ethics', delivered by Dean Inge to the British Science Guild, a body which, I may remark, represents applied rather than pure science. I should be surprised if the Dean had devoted as much time to the study of science as I have to that of Christianity (for I attended two Christian schools), yet I fear that a lecture by myself on Christian Ethics would be regarded by the Dean as at best black-legging, at worst blasphemy. For he has done me the honour to state that I am prejudiced concerning religion; though agnosticism, being a refusal to make up one's mind at all, is surely the very opposite of prejudice, which is the making-up of one's mind before hearing the evidence.

A fair proportion of the Dean's discourse was de-voted to diatribes against the Roman Catholic Church, which, it appears, is in several respects less scientific than the Protestant organizations. I confess that, as an impartial outsider, I hope that as long as there are an appreciable number of Protestants they will be balanced by some Catholics; for, while both bodies have been about equally hostile to truth, the Catholics have on the whole been kinder to beauty. And as long as the Anglican Prayer-Book includes prayers for rain and for the satisfactory functioning of the organs of the royal family, for a Dean to animadvert upon Lourdes is simply a case of the pot calling the kettle black.

In so far as the Dean exalts truth, attacks supernatural dualism, and realizes that evolution implies the rights of animals, I think that everyone here will be in agree-ment with him. How little importance is attached to truth as such in our society appears very clearly in a recent judgment of Mr. Justice Humphreys in a case where a beauty specialist sued a rival for using a phrase which he had invented to advertise his business. The Judge held that the phrase was arresting and original—for one thing, because it was obviously untrue—and that it came within the Copyright Act. I do not think that he would have adopted so complacent an attitude had the phrase been obscene or seditious, and I doubt if a State permeated by scientific ethic would allow its courts to be used to support private property in lies. But with regard to the more detailed applications of biology to ethics, and especially in regard to his views on eugenics, I am afraid that I am a better Christian than the Dean. Perhaps I may be excused for speaking at some length on this subject because I have a considerable first-hand knowledge of animal and plant breeding, and have to some small extent advanced knowledge concerning heredity.

Let us first turn to the facts which are known with certainty. We know the laws which govern the inheritance of a number of defects. Some of these, like colour-blindness, are trivial, provided locomotive drivers and navigators of ships can be so tested as to exclude colour-blind men from these occupations. Others, such as short fingers, are unsightly, and may be a serious handicap. A third class, such as haemophilia (failure of the blood to coagulate) and some types of deaf-mutism, are dangerous to life, or else make a normal and useful life impossible. Now, these maladies are inherited in several different ways, and the type of inheritance determines the possibility or otherwise of eugenic action with regard to them. If all short-fingered persons were massacred to-morrow, this condition would be pretty completely abolished; but if all the deaf-mutes were killed off, it would take hundreds of generations before the proportion of them in the general population was halved. Now, I think that bearers of the former kind of hereditary complaints should be warned as to the type of children that they are likely to beget, and given every possible opportunity to avoid doing so; but I do not think that in the present state of public opinion any compulsion should be exerted on them. The time for that may come if attempts spread over several generations to persuade them to limit their families are a failure. But about the same time public opinion will perhaps be ripe for the official discouragement, in the interests of hygiene, of deans and others who spread the view that any but a very small class of diseases can be cured by prayer.

The inheritance of other desirable and undesirable characters is far less clearly understood. Feeble-mindedness is fairly strongly inherited, but unfortunately it is generally inherited in such a way that the segregation or massacre of the feeble-minded, even if continued for several generations, would not stamp it out. The feeble-minded, unless they mate with one another, do not necessarily produce feeble-minded children. If, therefore, the feeble-minded are to be segregated, it should be in their own interests, and because they are unfit to bring up a family, quite as much as on eugenical grounds.

But the most controversial and, to my mind, the least scientifically grounded of the proposals of the Dean and other eugenists who think like him relate not to a few small groups of the population, but to large numbers. In the first place, he congratulates the United

States on stopping the flood of immigration from Southern and Eastern Europe. Now, politically this may be a wise measure. The countrymen of Lenin and Mussolini probably do not make such good Babbits as the races of North-Western Europe. And, on the whole, they do not score as highly in so-called intelligence tests of the particular type current in the United States. Whether such a failure has any significance could probably be determined by the scientific methods which are being applied to such tests by Spearman and his pupils in England. But even if the average Italian is stupider than the average Swede, which may be the case, either or both of the following facts may still be true. Genius of certain types may be commoner among Italians than Swedes, and, as the result of crossing these two peoples, a type in many ways finer than either may be produced. This is certainly the general rule with animals and plants, and history suggests that it is true of men. Until these possibilities have been disproved, the exclusion of Southern Europeans from the United States cannot be justified on eugenic grounds. And if, as is very possible, they are better adapted than the inhabitants of Northern Europe for life in the Southern States, it may be an extremely short-sighted measure.

The same criticism applies to the question of the differential birth-rate in different social groups within the same State. It is true that in England the rich breed more slowly than the average and the skilled than the unskilled labourer, and that infantile and other mortality does not compensate for this difference. This phenomenon has gone on for only about two generations, and it is very probable that, with further social progress, it will cease; for in Stockholm, where the poor do not live in slums and birth-control is pretty universally practised, the rich have rather more children than the poor. Although it is certainly not scientifically proven, it seems likely that there is a correlation between wealth and the hereditary factors determining intelligence, because the well-to-do include many families of the professional classes in whom intelligence is undoubtedly hereditary, and the unskilled labourers include the majority of the feeble-minded. We do not yet know enough about the inheritance of mental ability to be able to say that a few generations of selection against it would weed it out to an appreciable extent, though this may quite probably be the case. But if we grant the case of the extreme eugenist, what is the remedy? The Dean would like to penalize the slum-dwellers who still produce large families, and other eugenists (though few, if any, scientific students of heredity) have condemned the spending of public funds to ameliorate the lot of the poor on similar grounds. If such is really the teaching of biology, there is a serious conflict between science and the dictates of the conscience of most enlightened men and women. And this alleged conflict is one ground for the distrust of science and its teachings which is very widely felt.

In my own opinion, the dictates of biology are exactly opposite, and on the whole in line with those of humanitarian ethics. If a difference in effective fertility exists between the rich and the poor, it seems to me profoundly illogical to attempt to remedy it by making the rich richer and the poor poorer. It is true that such an attempt might succeed if the poor were made so poor as to bring their infantile mortality up to about 50 per cent. But that would lower their physique and also create foci of disease, which would attack the rich. It would be better to send armoured cars through the slums from time to time, with special instructions to fire upon women and children. The correct remedy for the differential birth-rate would seem to be such a raising of the economic standards of the poor as would give them the same economic incentives to family limitation as exist among the rich, and such an equalization of educational and other opportunities as would lessen these latter incentives. The example of Stockholm shows that the differential birth-rate need not exist in a highly civilized community. I have stated elsewhere my personal views on the economic and other measures which would serve to equalize the birth-rates in different classes. As they have perhaps a somewhat political flavour, I shall not repeat them here. Suffice it to say that they do not commend themselves to the Dean of St. Paul's.

Other self-styled eugenists take a still more extreme view of innate human inequality. They suppose that moral qualities are inherited to much the same degree as physical and intellectual. It is true that brothers resemble one another in these respects about as much as in physical and intellectual qualities, but this is probably largely a matter of environment. It is, after all, a matter of common sense that it is easier to make a bad boy good than a stupid boy clever. Human experience has agreed to attach the social sanctions of praise and blame to qualities on which environment has a fairly large influence, and on the whole scientific observation goes to confirm common sense. There is probably such a thing as ineradicable moral imbecility, just as there is an acquired moral imbecility due to lethargic encephalitis; but these would seem to be a good deal rarer than

hereditary stupidity. Science does not, of course, support the doctrine of human perfectibility. But it does
tend to uphold the view that this doctrine is much more
nearly true in the sphere of ethics than in that of intellect—in other words, that mankind is more readily
modified by moral than intellectual education. And of
the principles of moral education we know very little.
We know, indeed, that such an education based on
religion is by no means an infallible guide to conduct,
even in an age of faith. In an age of reason it often
results in young people, who generally lose their faith
at a critical period of their lives, supposing that there
is no rational basis for right conduct. We know, both
from individual cases elsewhere and from the great example of the third French Republic, that such an education can be successfully conducted on purely secular
lines. But it should, I believe, be one of the principal
functions of an Ethical Society to investigate the relative
efficacy of different types of ethical propaganda. My
own small experience suggests that there are great individual differences between different children in this
respect: some, for example, being greatly moved by the
stories of noble lives; others, who may yet readily absorb
example or abstract precepts, being very little so.

But to return to eugenics: if a great deal which to my
mind is both unscientific and immoral has been advo-
cated in its name, I am certain that it has a very great
future as an ethical principle. The more we learn as to
what desirable qualities are inheritable, the more we
should seek these qualities in our own spouses. Now,
one does not fall in love as the result of a system of
marking beauty, intelligence, virtue, and so on, each
counting for so much. But one does so as the result of

the weight which one has given in one's appreciation of the other sex to these various qualities. As a biological outlook becomes commoner this weight will tend to vary. Length of pedigree will seem less important than soundness, wealth than health, education than intelligence. But just because eugenics is an ethical principle, it should begin at home, like charity, and influence individual conduct before public policy.

Hygiene and eugenics are, in all probability, only the first of a series of new spheres of duty which biology is opening up. To take but one example: at the present moment our only clear duty to animals is to spare them obvious physical suffering. As we learn about their psychology we shall know better. It is quite possibly as cruel to keep a pet rat in a light and airy cage as to lock a dog in the cellar all day; and it is already the duty of everyone who keeps animals to acquaint himself with the elementary principles governing nutrition.

Ever since the utilitarian movement ethics have become more and more a matter of the calculation of consequences. We may reject the criterion of the greatest happiness of the greatest number, either because it is incalculable, or because happiness does not appear a sufficiently noble goal; but we are all, or nearly all, agreed that actions must be judged by their probable consequences, and not by any code which does not envisage such consequences. We have not yet gone very far towards calculating these consequences scientifically. In the doubtful cases only scientific method will help us. The question, for example, whether I should subscribe £1 to the Cancer Hospital or the Cancer Research Campaign depends on the value which I attribute to research. As a careful study of the paths by which cancer cells migrate from the breast has been largely instrumental in reducing the mortality from breast cancer to about 10 per cent. in the early operated cases, I am personally in favour of research; but I have not got the quantitative knowledge of how far a pound goes in research and treatment respectively which would enable me to form a definite judgment on the question. And in the present state of affairs any statistics available would be directed to proving a case rather than arriving at the truth.

If it is our duty to envisage, so far as possible, the consequences of our actions, it follows that we must deliberately attempt to suppress our emotions until this investigation is completed. Bentham attempted to do so, but with the passing of utilitarianism and the growing realization of the importance of the emotional side of the human mind few have attempted to follow his example. Yet only on such lines can scientific method be applied directly to ethical problems. Such an application can hardly be said as yet to exist. We do not realize how largely a scientifically based code of ethics would depend on statistical data. The moment we begin to study statistics new duties appear. Let us take an apparently trivial choice—shall I buy a glass or pottery bowl for my flowers? I turn to the occupational mortality statistics, and find that, though the mortality of glass workers is above the average, that of potters is still higher. Other things being equal, I ought to buy glass. If we knew enough no choice would be trivial, and it is our duty to acquire the knowledge which will enable us to moralize our everyday actions, both by the study of available statistics and by encouraging statistical inquiry elsewhere.

But does science reduce ethics to mere calculation? It is true that science from its nature can only say what is, was, or will be, and not what ought to be. It cannot, of course, give an answer to the question, "Why should I be good?" There is, in the long run, no answer to that question, for a previously good action ceases to be good in so far as it is directed to any non-ethical end. But our views as to the status of good action are profoundly affected by our views of the universe. If good corresponds to nothing more objective than our individual preferences, the good life appears to us more heroic perhaps, but also rather futile. Now, the tendency of science in its early stages, as it cleared away the jungle of mythology, was to leave the human individual apparently isolated. Eighteenth-century Rationalism, which did not suceed in replacing Christianity, though it affected human thought profoundly, was such a philosophy of isolated individuals.

It seems to me that modern science makes this isolation far less plausible than it seemed two hundred, or even fifty, years ago. The older science either supposed that the universe and the human body were mere machines, or that they were machines to some extent guided by God and the soul respectively. No facts are known to science which give any serious support to the latter view. But it does not follow that the former is correct. The human body is composed of cells, and the cells of atoms. Many of the cells can be cultivated outside the body. They have a life of their own, and can live a Robinson Crusoe kind of existence in suitable surroundings. Hence they do not derive their life from the soul or anything outside themselves. But their co-operation manifests itself in the life of the whole man, and more particularly in his consciousness. A study of the effects on the mind of brain injuries makes it fairly certain that consciousness depends not on any one cell, which might be the seat of the soul, but on a very large number. Yet every attempt to find forces other than those of ordinary physics operating within the organism has been a complete failure, and the success of modern medicine, and animal and plant breeding, are at least pragmatic justifications of that point of view. The mutual relations of the atoms constituting the cell seem also to be describable in terms of physics and chemistry. Nevertheless, life, organic unity, and consciousness are facts a good deal more certain than the existence of cells and atoms. It is clear that aggregates of a certain kind do manifest qualities which we cannot observe in their components.

The doctrine of emergence, which is widely held to-day, is that aggregates may have qualities, such as life or consciousness, which are quite foreign to their parts. This doctrine may conceivably be true, but it is radically opposed to the spirit of science, which has always attempted to explain the complex in terms of the simple, and has on the whole succeeded. We do not find obvious evidence of life or mind in so-called inert matter, and we naturally study them most easily where they are most completely manifested; but if the scientific point of view is correct, we shall ultimately find them, at least in rudimentary forms, all through the universe.

Now, if the co-operation of some thousands of millions of cells in our brain can produce our consciousness, the idea becomes vastly more plausible that the co-operation of humanity, or some sections of it, may determine what Comte called a Great Being. Just as, according to the teachings of physiology, the unity of the body is not due to a soul superadded to the life of the cells, so the superhuman, if it existed, would be nothing external to man, or even existing apart from human co-operation. But to my mind the teaching of science is very emphatic that such a Great Being may be a fact as real as the individual human consciousness, although, of course, there is no positive scientific evidence for the existence of such a being. And it seems to me that everywhere ethical experience testifies to a super-individual reality of some kind. The good life, if not necessarily self-denial, is always self-transcendence. This idea is, of course, immanent in the higher religions, but the objects of religious worship retain the characteristics of nature-gods or deified human individuals. It was more satisfactorily expressed by Comte; but there is much in Positivism as originally conceived by him which seems unnecessarily arbitrary.

Just because any formulation of the nature of such a being has ultimately fallen below the best in our own moral consciousness, religions, though at first a help, later become a hindrance to ethical progress, and we too shall do no good by premature theorizing. But just as, starting from the basis of chemistry, biochemists are gradually explaining the phenomena of life, so from a basis of psychology our descendants may build up a scientific ethics which may perhaps be at the same time a scientific theology. Much of modern psychology is, I suspect, mere cerebral physiology. I do not see, for example, why we need postulate any 'Unconscious' other than certain parts of our own brains. It may well be that the main psychology of the future will be social psychology, just as I believe that in fifty years the most important branch of chemistry will be biochemistry. In this way we may hope that ethics will ultimately be brought within the sphere of science.

At present the only branch of science which is concerned with moral conduct as such is anthropology. One branch of that science is concerned with human societies, and analyses the various factors influencing conduct in them. Most of these analyses, of course, bear on the simple institutions of primitive peoples. The anthropologist can observe them from outside, and need not take sides in a dispute, say, between a witch-doctor and a witch. Anthropologists are generally agreed that the magic and religion of primitive peoples are essential parts of their social system, and hold that missionaries destroy the very foundations of society when they introduce Christianity or Islam. Now, the same argument is applied by certain anthropologically minded persons to our own society. They hold that, although most of Christian dogma is untrue, the Church is as essential to the stability of European society as the fetish-house to that of West African. We cannot dismiss this point of view because it is somewhat derogatory to human nature. If science does not endorse the prophet's view that 'The heart is deceitful above all things and desperately wicked', it is equally far from regarding it as entirely perfectible by a change of environment.

The first obvious point that arises is that, while the anthropologist might regard the Church as essential for the stability of society, he would certainly not regard its moral code as correct. For the behaviour of Christians, like that of other men, has always been a compromise between that dictated by their moral code and their private inclinations. But that moral code has never —at least, among those Christian peoples who have advanced civilization — been purely Christian. The governing classes in Europe have generally kept before them the ideal of honour in one of its many forms. This is an ideal based on pride rather than humility, or self-realization rather than self-denial. It has generally been linked with some form of family pride or patriotism. It has, of course, had its aberrations, but they have been a natural reaction against the abjection into which the Church has attempted to force the spirit of man. In the somewhat modified form of sportsmanship this code is current among all classes in England to-day. I am not a sportsman myself on weekdays; but, as I do not call myself a miserable sinner on Sundays, I can, at least, attempt to practise a more rational morality during seven days a week.

Our anthropologist, then, would have to demand the existence of a non-Christian moral ideal beside that of Christianity, trusting to human weakness to see that neither was too strictly enforced. Now, the present moral crisis is due, among other things, to the demand for a moral code which shall be intellectually respectable. The existence of that demand, encouraged as it is by the success of rationalism in the sphere of science, is no doubt a serious matter, but the demand is growing daily. And it comes at a time when applied science has created so many new moral problems that the morality of our ancestors must in any case be drastically revised. Until now poverty and disease have been inevitable evils to be palliated by the exercise of the virtue of charity. With the means at our disposal to-day we could abolish all poverty and most disease. But the moral energy required for these purposes is still directed into less efficient channels. In the same way our sexual morality has been adjusted to produce the high birth-rate demanded by a high death-rate. It is now being rather painfully altered to meet the new social demands upon it.

If, then, our moral code must, in any case, be recast, we are justified in demanding that it be recast on a rational basis. The impossible demands attributed to the Christian God made it necessary to create the Devil to counterbalance him. A morality based on science would be quantitative, as was Greek morality. The ideal of the Greeks was τὸ μέτριον, a word often translated as the mean, but, perhaps, more accurately as the measured. This ideal, however, only applied to social conduct—for example, to spending one's income on the pursuit of pleasure. In this sphere it is quite clear that science will be able to help us. Economics and hygiene are already beginning to do so. But even Greek morality as we find it codified, for example, in Aristotle's *Ethics* —was not merely quantitative. A man might eat too much, or expose himself to too much danger, and so on, but he could not have too much knowledge or too much moral intuition. And Christian ethics replaced those of the ancients largely because they made unlimited demands on the human spirit, and it does somehow respond to such demands. I doubt if any morality which does not do so will get the maximum response from man.

A scientific morality which proclaimed that man existed as part of a greater aggregate could yet admit that he had claims as an individual. The cells in our own body co-operate in its life, but yet live, so to speak,

very comfortably as compared with individualistic pro-
tozoa. And as long as I act, in general, as a member of
society, I believe that I shall do so the better, and not
the worse, for having a good dinner and taking holidays.
If the Great Being is wholly independent of individual
men, their well-being must be disregarded in its service.
If it exists through them, and only through them, their
rights are its rights. The morality of the future will, I
believe, contain elements of both Greek and Christian
moralities. The vague conception of the mean will be
rendered exact by quantitative science, and the ideal of
self-sacrifice will perhaps be rationalized as co-operation in a real and intelligible super-individual reality.

To-day we are very far from any such blessed condition. Yet we can begin, as I have shown, to apply
scientific method both to individual moral problems
and to the problem of morality itself. The time required
for so great a task must be measured on a historical,
perhaps even on a geological, time-scale. But it represents the unification of human effort, the marriage of
the mind and the heart, the moralization of science,
and the rationalization of ethics. Let us be thankful if
we can play any part, however small, in so great an
enterprise.

THE PLACE OF SCIENCE IN WESTERN CIVILIZATION *

WESTERN civilization rests on applied science. By that statement I do not mean either of two propositions which could not be upheld. I do not mean, in the first place, that all civilization rests upon science, and I do not mean that Western civilization rests only upon science. In the last lecture of this series Mr. Bertrand Russell pointed out that Western civilization is based upon a number of other things besides science. It is, I think, important to realize that Western civilization has been largely based upon the application of science for a much longer period than the one hundred and fifty years which are commonly said to have elapsed since the beginning of the industrial revolution.

Let us take a very characteristic feature of Western civilization: the colonization and conquest of large portions of the world by the inhabitants of Western Europe. That event would have taken place, not perhaps quite to the present extent, but certainly on a very large scale, even if steam-engines had never been invented. America and Australia would, as now, be largely populated by white people. The reason for that is that long-distance navigation was made possible by the application of science which had developed, not in the last one hundred and fifty years, but in the last five hundred;

* A lecture delivered before the Fabian Society at Kingsway Hall, Kingsway, London, W.C., on Thursday, October 25, 1928.

by the application of the science of geography and all those scientific principles which are involved in such great inventions as the compass, the sextant, and the chronometer. It is, therefore, true to say that Western civilization is largely based on applied science, even if we go back to the early seventeenth and eighteenth centuries. It is the application of science which more than any other feature differentiates Western civilization from other civilizations of the past or present; but it is also, as Mr. Russell pointed out, based upon Greek, Roman, and Jewish ideas.

Now, there is one important difference between the position of science and of these borrowed ideas in our system. It is necessary for anybody who is to function at all efficiently, even in the lowest position in our civilization, to understand, to some extent, the meaning of a number of Greek, Roman, and Jewish ideas. There are very few people in London who do not understand, to some extent, the meaning of the Greek idea of athletics; the Jewish idea of God; the Roman idea of law. But they need not know anything whatever about scientific ideas, although they all enjoy the benefits of science; they drive in motor-cars, they get killed by high explosives, and so on. As we shall see, without the very faintest knowledge of scientific ideas they can rise to the very highest posts in the Church or in the State.

Science has furnished the material basis of our civilization, but its ideas are still pre-scientific, and that is one of the principal reasons for the extraordinary misuse of applied science which is so characteristic of our age. The late war is a very good example of this misuse. I shall attempt to show that the future of Western civilization depends, to a very large extent, on whether it can incorporate into itself not only scientific inventions, but scientific ideas and a scientific outlook.

It is an elementary fact which no reader will doubt, that the progress of society depends, among other things, on the progressive application of science. Unfortunately, this idea is not realized by our ruling classes to-day. In face of a new application of science it has two ideas. First of all, 'Can we suppress it?' Secondly, 'Can we tax it?' Let us take some examples which will serve to illustrate this attitude.

In recent years there have been three great applications of biology—rather elementary biology, no doubt, but nevertheless biology—namely, antiseptics, contraceptives, and poison gas. Antiseptics are allowed in certain cases. They are allowed in order to prevent infection of open wounds by a certain group of organisms; but they are not allowed to prevent venereal disease; or, if they are allowed, they must be sold without any instructions as to their use. Now, at the present time venereal diseases kill a great many more people per year than would die of infected wounds during peace-time if antiseptics were forbidden altogether. It is therefore clear that the major field of application of antiseptics has been very largely closed by State action. With regard to contraceptives, they may be forbidden altogether, as some kinds are, for example, in France or (theoretically) in the United States of America; or they may be frowned upon with more or less severity by the Government, as is the case in this country. The result is that the only means available of regulating the population, a means which might be of immense social value if it were directed, is allowed to be used in the most haphazard and unsatisfactory manner. Thirdly, we come

to poisonous gases. Mustard gas, or dichlor-ethyl sul-
phide, is the most humane weapon ever invented. Of
the casualties from mustard gas during the late war
there were 170,000 in the British Army alone. Three
per cent. or less died, and less than 1 per cent. were
permanently incapacitated—a very low proportion compared with the casualties from other weapons. Perhaps
it is for that reason that its use has been condemned
by the enlightened representatives of almost all civilized
nations. As might, however, be expected, the wicked
Bolsheviks would not consent to this humane action.*

Let us next consider three recent applications of
chemistry and physics, namely, the internal combus-
tion engine, artificial silk, and radio communication.
Motor vehicles, as some of you are rich enough to know,
are heavily taxed; and that tax goes, to a very large extent, not as it should do, to the upkeep of roads, but
to remove the burden of taxation and rates from such
industries as railways, which the motor vehicle is tending to render obsolete. Incidentally, the system of taxation of motor vehicles bears all the marks of having been
designed by a very meticulous lunatic in order to prevent the manufacture in this country of cars of the type
which could best be sold in the British Dominions.
Artificial silk, again, is being taxed, and the taxation serves
to remove the burden from obsolescent industries of other
kinds. Finally, the State wireless telegraph service is to
be handed over to the cable companies because the
latter are losing money.

It is clear, then, that the general policy, no doubt
not stated in so many words, of the present Government, and of Governments in the past, is to prevent,

* I am informed that they, too, have now agreed to forgo its use.

as far as possible, new applications of science, either to life or to industry. England is an industrial country, and if it is to be fed it must keep up with the rest of the world in the application of science to industry. The only alternative is to reduce the population, but that also, as we saw, is being discouraged. Now such an attitude, although ridiculous, is perfectly natural, because the ruling classes in this country are ignorant of the results of scientific work and still more grossly ignorant of the mental attitude which has led to scientific discoveries. Let us take some examples of their ignorance of the actual results of science.

One of the classical examples which is always quoted on these occasions, and which I take from the late Mr. Bateson's Collected Essays, is this: During the war the Home Secretary defended the Government for permitting the importation of fats into Germany on the ground that the discovery that glycerine could be made from fat was a very recent advance in chemistry. Actually that discovery was made in 1779! Up till the war I do not suppose that a pint of glycerine had ever been made from anything but fat. During the war, however, the Germans discovered a way of inducing yeast to make it from sugar. The real point of that joke is that there are probably very few British citizens who did not, during the war, lose a friend as the result of the extra casualties caused by that kind of ignorance in our Government. Let us take another example.

In 1926 a paper was read at the British Association in which the author described a compound of helium and mercury. *The Times* came out with its usual slightly comic leading article on the British Association in which it described this 'startling announcement'. It had been a startling announcement when it was made twenty months before in the columns of *Nature*, but since then there had been a considerable amount of discussion on the subject, and several other similar compounds had been described. When the level of scientific information in the columns of *The Times* reaches that of the *Berliner Tageblatt* or the Moscow *Pravda* I shall be inclined to read it, but till then I shall continue to read the *Herald* and the *Express*. Their scientific news is at least more amusing than that of *The Times*. However, the majority of our governing classes, I believe, take *The Times* quite seriously, and as there is no demand for up-to-date scientific information among its readers *The Times*, very naturally, takes little trouble to furnish it. The other daily papers, as far as I know, are no better than *The Times*.

There are certain exceptional individuals in our governing classes who know a little science, these including some of the men at the head of our more successful industries; for example, Lord Melchett. But the politicians, I think, are pretty universally ignorant of it. The attitude of the majority of politicians on these matters may, I think, be summed up in the immortal words of Sir Auckland Geddes: 'In politics, in the affairs with which Governments have to deal, it is not accurate knowledge that matters—it is emotion'! A minority of politicians, however, do possess a certain amount of accurate knowledge, but that accurate knowledge is almost invariably of law or of economics.

Ignorance of science among the governing classes was relatively unimportant so long as the State did not interfere in industry. It is serious now, when the policy of the Government, as we saw, is to strangle new industries; and when the principle of State interference in industry is admitted and practised by all the parties. But in the case of a government control and ownership of industry, in the case of Socialism, such ignorance would be disastrous. If a Socialist Government in control of the industries of this country knows no more than the Conservative Government either of science or even of those persons in the scientific world who possess the information which they want, the result will, I think, be a calamity. Socialism, I believe, will fail if it is administered by men and women as ignorant of science as the present Civil Service, and I am inclined to believe, for that reason and not on political grounds, that Socialism has a better chance in Germany than in any of the other great industrial States. In Germany scientific education is very widespread, and there are probably enough Socialists in Germany with a scientific and technical knowledge (as opposed to the economic knowledge which is reasonably widespread among Socialists in England) to enable German industry to work in the event of a refusal of non-Socialist scientists and technicians to assist. I very much doubt whether the same is the case in England. If Socialism is to succeed in Britain, it seems to me that it is a necessary preliminary condition, first of all, that a knowledge of science should be spread among Socialists; and secondly, that a knowledge of Socialism should be spread among scientists. Incidentally, I think that this would be very good both for science and for Socialism.

I do not mean to suggest that the Cabinet, like Mr. Lloyd George's, should include a few university professors who have shown a greater turn for administration than for research. What is needed in this country is that young men and women, looking forward to a political career, should study science seriously. I should like to see the students of Ruskin, for example, imitating the Communists in the Sverdlov University at Moscow. In that university half of their first year is devoted to general science, mainly cosmology and the study of evolution; in their next two years they spend a good deal of time on chemistry and physics, largely from the technical point of view; and in their fourth year they have another special course of science. I happened to go round the biological laboratories in which they worked. I could see at once that their practical work was quite as good as a great deal of the practical work which is done by those in this country who are taking up science as a career. There was no sham about it. In consequence, assuming the present Russian *régime* to last for another fifteen years, you will, for the first time in the history of the world, have a scientifically educated governing class at the head of a great State. What the result of that will be I do not pretend to know. It will, undoubtedly, be interesting. It may be a little too interesting for this country!

The usual course of study for would-be politicians is, I believe, history. I think that the study of history is somewhat fallacious owing to the enormous changes which have taken place in the last fifty years. For example, up till fifty years ago every State was based on the presupposition that most of the population would have to spend the greater part of their time in hard physical work. That is no longer the case. It seems to me that facts such as that make the lessons of history a little dubious in their application to modern problems.

So far I have spoken mainly about physics and chemistry and their applications. These sciences are valued, if not understood, by a considerable section of the ruling class. The reason for that is quite simple. Those sciences lead to inventions which enable individuals to make fortunes. They do not, of course, enable the individuals who make the fundamental discoveries to make fortunes, but they make fortunes for somebody. And, therefore, like other means of making large fortunes—the Calcutta Sweep, for example—they appeal to all that is best in the hearts of our rich men! Now biology does not lead to the making of very large fortunes by anybody; fairly large fortunes by some successful doctors, no doubt, but not of the order of magnitude of those which are obtained from applied chemistry or physics; and therefore biology is not greatly valued in this country or anywhere in Western Europe. It is valued in England mainly in so far as it is necessary for efficient medicine; but in certain other countries, notably in Denmark and the United States, it is also valued because it can be applied to agriculture. That idea does not seem to have dawned seriously in England, although this country is the centre of the British Commonwealth, which produces a great deal more food and other agricultural products than any other State in the world. In spite of that fact we have, for example, in the entire British Empire only two professors of genetics, although pretty nearly every university in the United States has a professor of that science, and the Union of Socialist Soviet Republics is crawling with them.

In this country, however, there is very little feeling for pure biology. The exceptions in Western civilization are Messrs. Carnegie and Rockefeller, who have given very large sums for the endowment of biological work. One can only suppose that they have made so much money that they actually wanted to spend it on something which would give no financial return to anybody. However, their attitude is not generally shared in Britain. Some time ago Mr. Rockefeller offered a considerable sum for biological work in London University if the other half could be found in this country, but it has not been found. I have no reason to suppose that it will be. Moreover, throughout Western Europe, and still more perhaps in the United States, biology may not be taught to children seriously; that is to say, it may not be taught to them in connection with their own lives. Human physiology and genetics upset quite a number of our prejudices. The physiology of digestion, reproduction, and excretion are indecent; the physiology of the brain is irreligious. On the other hand, chemistry, physics, and certain branches of botany have no immediate bearing on conduct, and therefore they do not come into conflict with any deep-seated prejudices, and are taught in schools. It has, moreover, been found that a good course of systematic botany, taught on the lines of Greek grammar, can immunize the average child against any further interest in science. It is, therefore, not in the least surprising that very little interest is taken in biology and very little attention paid to biological argument among the governing classes, or even the working classes of this country.

Biological arguments are quite useless for practical purposes. A very few politicians may—though I know of no evidence of it—think in terms of physics and chemistry on rare occasions; none has ever thought in terms of biology. But yet it would seem that, as human beings are alive, the State should take some cognizance of biological principles. We have, it is true, a department humorously called the Ministry of Health, but it is not realized that State action influences the national health except through such agencies as drains, water supply, and medical officers of health.

Let us look at a few facts as to how State action actually influences the public health. The State has already begun to interfere very seriously in economics by means of tariffs, subsidies, and the like. Now, occupations differ vastly in their health. For example, if you take the average death-rate as 100, agricultural labourers have a death-rate of 68, and tin miners of 433; that is to say, they die a good deal more than four times as rapidly as the ordinary person. In face of such facts the State preserves a delightful impartiality. From the point of view of health, some of its actions in the last ten years have, undoubtedly, been satisfactory. The subsidy on beet sugar has, one supposes, brought a few more people back to the land, where they are healthier than in the town. The tariff on watches has, presumably, encouraged the watchmaking trade, which happened to be a healthy one. But, on the other hand, the Coalition Government gave a subsidy to assist the Cornish tin mines which, as we saw, kill people in a most efficient way; and there are protections for parts of the glass and pottery trades, which are exceedingly unhealthy, and for trades involving metal-grinding, which are still worse. In the arguments for and against safeguarding such facts as those were, I believe, never brought up, the reason being that politicians, quite regardless of their party, are dominated by economic considerations when they act rationally at all. In the future, as in-

K

dustry develops more and more, there will be more potentially dangerous occupations. As the Government has agreed to intervene in industry it is its plain duty, as it seems to me, to favour the healthy industries at the expense of the least healthy. The position of really unhealthy trades, such as the glass and pottery trade, under a Socialist Government is one which demands the most earnest consideration by those who are trying to plan the details of such a Government.

There is one attempted application of biology to politics, and that is the eugenics movement. If you take the Eugenics Society as typical of that movement the conclusion to which most of their spokesmen have been led is that the poor, on the whole, carry an undesirable heredity and that they are breeding too fast. Generally, therefore, members of that Society believe in measures which would tend to slow down the breeding of various sections of the poor, and many of them would like to subsidize breeding among the rich who, it is believed, contain superior stocks.

Now, let us suppose that all the premises believed in by Dean Inge, Major Darwin, and the like are true. I do not regard them as scientifically proven, but it is quite possible that they are very largely correct. It seems to me that the conclusions to be drawn from them are exactly the opposite of those drawn by those gentlemen. If the structure of society is such that the best stocks in it are being bred out, we must change that structure. If the rich limit their families it is, largely, I believe, for two reasons: they want to be able to leave money to their children and they want to be able to afford an expensive education for them. To my mind, the obvious moral to be drawn is that it would be a eugenic measure to abolish hereditary wealth, and have one, and only one, school system for all the population. If I held the same views on biology as Dean Inge and Major Darwin I should be a rather extreme kind of Socialist. Unfortunately, those gentlemen have not been able to convince me that the poor are quite as bad as they paint them, and therefore I do not think that the present social order is quite as strongly condemned as I should otherwise be compelled to think. But I do think that it is exceedingly probable that some forms, at any rate, of Socialism would be very considerably less dysgenic than the capitalism under which we live. The biological facts put forward by the Eugenics Society would be a very good weapon in the Socialist armoury, if biological arguments had any political value. But, as I have pointed out already, they have no political value. Nevertheless, as an intellectual curiosity I put that point of view before you.

Such, then, is the present position of Western civilization. There has been a complete failure to integrate into its intellectual structure the scientific ideas which have furnished its material structure. There are two alternatives, as it seems to me, before it. In the first place, scientific ideas may not be accepted by the ruling classes. If so, one can only be quite sure that the future will hold a few more little surprises like the late war, resulting from the applications of science. Let me take one fairly probable event which may happen within the lifetime of some here, namely, the production of synthetic food on a commercial scale. I think that some of my audience will live to see the production of edible fats and oils from coal and mineral oil, and the production of sugar and starch from such materials as woodpulp and straw. These inventions, if the ruling classes in Western civilization do not sit up and take notice, will be exploited by individual rich men, or individual States; and the result will be so enormous a dislocation of exchange, such disastrous efforts upon agriculture and husbandry, that there will inevitably be revolutions and wars. Even now a very considerable fraction —how much I do not know—of our industrial troubles is due to the obsolescence of certain of our industries; the failure of the railways, for example, to pay adequate dividends without being backed up by permission to raise their tariffs, to get off rates and so on, in face of the competition of the motor vehicle. I think it is highly probable that science will produce new weapons of a very disagreeable character for use in war. I do not think they will produce anything very much worse than the present high explosives; but it is perfectly clear that there are going to be extremely nasty surprises during the next war, and that the only attitude of governments in the application of science to war is that they should get in first and that they should forgo any inventions which would tend to make war more humane. It is certain that quite a number of new vices will arise as the result of the application of science. It is only four years ago, for example, that a Bavarian chemist discovered how to synthesize cocaine from simple coal-tar products, a discovery which of course renders any attempt at the regulation of cocaine production from plants more or less nugatory. Anyone who buys the right scientific journal and has a slight scientific knowledge can make it if he wants to. And no doubt very soon we shall have synthetic morphine. A large number of organic compounds is constantly being put on the market. Some will, no doubt, be the basis of some very elegant vices which will be tackled by governments after they have been in existence for a generation or so. By that time they will be well rooted and there will be great difficulty in dealing with them.

But far more serious, to my mind, is the spiritual decay which is going on now and will go on as long as our intellectual attitude does not alter. Religion is declining for the very simple reason that all religions are full of obsolete science of various kinds; especially obsolete cosmology and obsolete psychology. It may be that there is a core in religion which is independent of scientific criticism. I am rather inclined to take that view, but I would add that the present apparent lull in the conflict between science and religion is exceedingly deceptive. Science has largely dislodged religion from its front line of trenches. The old view of the structure of the universe is universally given up. At present what is happening is that psychologists are hauling up their guns into position with a view to an assault on the second line, namely, religious psychology.

Now, religion has attempted to counter this, not by retiring to what may be, and perhaps is, an impregnable position, but by trying to adapt itself to this world by concentration on social work, and so on. In the past it has been an historical function of religion to hold up before humanity a transcendental ideal, however imperfectly presented. If the only function of religion is to establish the Kingdom of God on earth, the Socialists say, 'We can do it better than you'. To-day it seems to me that transcendental ideals which take men out of the field of ordinary life are only active in the realms of science and art. But most artists do not reach anything but a limited public. The exception, a very important exception, due not to art but to science is in the case of music. For the first time in history, thanks to broadcasting, millions of people are hearing first-rate intellectual music performed by first-rate artists. That will have, I think, very great spiritual consequences, but I do not think that it will be sufficient to stem the general lack of belief in transcendental ideals, such as truth and beauty, which is going on. It is quite possible, I think, that as the ideals of pure science become more and more remote from those of the general public, science will tend to degenerate more and more into medical and engineering technology, just as art may degenerate into illustration and religion into ritual when they lose the vital spark. That tendency in science is going on to-day in many countries. It is very marked, I think, in Italy, where they have to-day great engineers, like Marconi, but no more great physicists like Galileo and Galvani. The result of such a tendency would be that gradually the flow of real invention would dry up. If so, we may hope that the spirit of inquiry will continue in Asia. In India to-day far more first-rate research in pure physics is being done than in the majority of European countries; but if the spirit of inquiry remains in Asia when it has petered out in Europe and North America, the outlook for Western civilization is not very hopeful.

There is a second alternative, and that is that a serious attempt will be made to incorporate scientific ideas, as well as scientific inventions, in our national and international life. That attempt is being made to-day in Russia. They have altered the ruling class. They did not try to educate the old one. Their attempts to apply science to life are crude, they are embryonic, sometimes ridiculous, like a good many other things in Russia; but they are being made in Russia and not seriously made anywhere else. Among the small fraction of the Russian population who read seriously, science and politics take the place which are taken in England and the United States by religion and sport. The children in the towns of Russia learn a great deal more science than the corresponding children in England, and they learn it not as a textbook subject like French grammar, but in relation to their ordinary life. If you go round the book-shops in central Moscow—there are plenty of book-shops there; a good many more per hundred yards than in central London—you will have a very long way to go before finding a book-shop whose window does not contain books on pure science. In about ten days in Moscow I found three such, but two contained books on technology. The public papers are full of science. The competition pages, for example, have picture puzzles. I noticed one which included pictures of Harvey, Einstein, and Newton among other people who had to be recognized. I do not think the average competitor in English papers is interested in that kind of thing. Workers' classes there are on the most magnificent scale, and they have real science and real experiments of a type which are not allowed by law to be demonstrated to medical students in this country. They attempt in every possible way to link up science with politics. For example, a shop-window display of books bearing on the trial of the Donetz colliery engineers was 'starring' a volume on the relation of geology to economics. They are trying to link up every branch of science with every branch of political life.

I do not say for one moment that Russia is a scientific State. I say that it purports to be a scientific State in the same way that the States of medieval Europe purported to be Christian. They were not fully Christian, but Christianity had an immense influence in them and was an enormously important part of their life. There is any amount of research being done in Russia. Innumerable young people of both sexes are going in for pure science for a number of reasons. First of all, because of the intense general interest in science. Secondly, because in Russia scientific workers are relatively, though not absolutely, much better off than they are in this country. Thirdly, because independent intellectual activity in many other spheres is much more hampered there than it is in pure science. There is an enormous interest in Russia in biology, because evolution is part of the Communist faith.

To take an example, in the whole world the only quantitative work on natural selection, as it actually happens in real life as opposed to the laboratory, is being done in Russia, mostly on crop plants and dandelions. In the scientific study of animal heredity Russia is ahead of all the rest of the world except the United States, and I think that in another ten years it will probably be ahead of the United States.

Now I am not going for one moment to suggest that there is not a very grave danger for science in so close an association with the State. It may possibly be that as a result of that association science in Russia will undergo somewhat the same fate as overtook Christianity after its association with the State in the time of Constantine. It is possible that it may lead to dogmatism in science and to the suppression of opinions which run counter to official theories, but it has not yet done so.

I will give you an example. Professor Berg, a Russian author, wrote a book on Nomogenesis giving an account of evolution on un-Darwinian lines — for example, natural selection was regarded as unimportant. The majority of scientific people in Russia, and the majority who had to do with the State publishing houses, thought the opinions expressed quite unsound, as I do, but they published the book. That, I think, shows that at the present time there is not a very serious suppression of scientific thought in Russia.

There is, you must remember, just the same danger in England. I could give you cases of experiments in human biology which cannot be done without ruining your career; or, at any rate, their results cannot be published. Quite a well-known British psychologist has made a number of extraordinarily interesting observations with regard to sexual life in human beings that would not only lose him his job, but probably cause suppression of whatever periodical published them for indecency, were they published. So that danger exists in societies of all kinds.

The test of the devotion of the Union of Socialist Soviet Republics to science will, I think, come when the accumulation of the results of human genetics, demonstrating what I believe to be the fact of innate human inequality, becomes important. I am a very strong believer in innate inequality, but I would like to point out that there is another source of innate inequality, namely, segregation, which is about as important as heredity in so far as concerns physically measurable characters like stature; and I have no doubt it is the same with regard to innate psychological characters. So a belief in innate inequality does not mean a belief in the omnipotence of heredity. But this belief is certainly incompatible with the sentimental and unscientific views often associated with Socialism. It seems to me, as I said before, that while the conclusions to be drawn from a study of human inequality are not necessarily favourable to capitalism, they are, at any rate, favourable to some forms of Socialism, though perhaps not to all forms.

It is quite certain, I think, that if the Union of Socialist Soviet Republics lasts for another ten years without an economic collapse, other States will imitate it to a greater or less extent. Whether it will last, I have no idea, though I see no reason to doubt it. I do not know any economics. My opinion as to whether it will last or not is worth no more than that of the editor of the *Daily Mail*. It is quite possible that the United States may take seriously to science. There is a large section of influential people there who are beginning to take science seriously; but there are certainly other possibilities there—Fundamentalism, Babbittism, and so on.

Now if we do manage to incorporate science into our ideas we shall, I think, be able to develop both the application of physics and chemistry and of biology very much more satisfactorily than is now the case, and a Socialist Government would be able to do very much more along these lines than is possible under the present system. But in addition there will be results of a kind other than material which will be at least equally important. I believe that if the average man and woman can realize the facts which are now known about his or her position as a component of the world, that realization will, to a very large extent, fill the emotional gap which is left by the collapse of the religious picture of the universe. There are complaints about the spiritual bankruptcy of the age in all kinds of circles. There is no such complaint among the ranks of scientific workers. The problem is to promote a society with scientific ideas while ensuring independence of thought for the scientific researcher. It is possible that that problem is insoluble: that a society can only assimilate a limited number of ideas at a time, and that, when its capacity for assimilation is reached it must take a rest in barbarism of some kind or other. But if that problem is soluble, it seems to me that the future of civilization is very bright. There is probably a limit to the immediate progress of applied physics and chemistry. The sources of readily available energy, coal and oil, are being exhausted, and it is possible that economies in the use of energy will not do very much more than compensate for that exhaustion. It is quite likely, I think, that even if things go fairly well for our civilization, a hundred or two hundred years hence the average real wage of the world will not be so very much greater than the average real wage in the United States to-day, although I sincerely hope that there will be a little more leisure. But if people want it to go, the vast majority of disease will go within the next one hundred years. By 'want it to go' I mean be willing to take a certain amount of trouble in order that disease should go; take up, in fact, a biological attitude. Take as much trouble, or even half as much trouble, about health as about wealth.

There is a limit to the possibilities of human health among people who will not take a scientific point of view about their own insides. But if in any community the large majority of people are able to take such a view, then I think that in one hundred years the average person ought to be able to go through life without passing any time in hospital, just as he goes through life now without passing any time in prison. There would be exceptions. There are exceptional people now who go into hospital for experimental purposes in order to clear up some bit of ignorance, and that I hope will be so one hundred years hence, just as now there are exceptional people who go to prison to clear up some bit of injustice.

Even now psychology is beginning to become scientific. I do not think that the results of scientific psychology are yet very clear, but if we start trying to take a scientific attitude about our own behaviour, looking at ourselves objectively, the first thing we do is to laugh, and that has an extremely good effect on our behaviour. In two hundred years I think we shall be in a position, in so far as we are willing to take a scientific point of view, to clear up our own characters as we can now, to a large extent, clear up our own health.

One last point. The scientific point of view is the point of view which has been taken up by scientific men, first, about their own problems and later about the problems of the world in general: a point of view which is finding every day a wider and wider applicability. Now the scientific man, as well as being intellectual, is a highly skilled manual labourer, and his point of view is probably not quite strange to other manual workers. I think it ought to find a very much greater sympathy among manual workers than the points of view which have been put forward by various groups of intellectuals in the past. He is a manual worker, but he is pursuing an ideal end, namely, Truth. The scientific point of view is lofty enough to satisfy any of the aspirations of the human spirit. I believe that the future of Western civilization depends upon whether or not it can assimilate that scientific point of view.

MAN'S DESTINY

IF, as I am inclined to suspect, the human will is to some small extent free, there is no such thing as a destiny of the human race. There is a choice of destinies. Even if our actions are irrevocably predetermined, we do not know our destiny. In either case, however, we can point to a limited number of probable fates for our species.

First let us consider the stage for our drama. The earth has existed for over a thousand million years.

During most of this period its surface temperature has not been very different from that now prevailing. The sun has not cooled down appreciably during that time, and it will probably be only a little cooler a million million years hence, though somewhere about that time it is quite likely that the earth's surface will be destroyed owing to the disruption of the moon by tidal forces.

Six hundred million years ago our ancestors were worms, ten thousand years ago they were savages. Both these periods are negligible compared with our possible future. Provided, therefore, that man has a future lasting for more than a few million years, we can at once say that our descendants may, for anything we can see to the contrary, excel us a great deal more than we excel worms or jellyfish.

There are, however, several alternatives to this prospect. A catastrophe of an astronomical order, such as a collision with a stray heavenly body, is unlikely. The earth has lasted a long time without any such disasters.

The sun may possibly swell up temporarily, as similar stars occasionally do. In this case the human race will be very rapidly roasted. A disease may arise which will wipe out all, or almost all, mankind. But there is nothing in science to make such up-to-date versions of the Apocalypse very probable.

Even if man does not perish in this dramatic manner, there is no reason why civilization should not do so. All civilization apparently goes back to a common source less than ten thousand years ago, possibly in Egypt. It is a highly complicated invention which has probably been made only once. If it perished it might never be made again.

When in the past its light was extinguished in one area—for example, when the Angles and Saxons wrecked Roman Britain—it could be lit again from elsewhere, as our savage ancestors were civilized from Italy and Ireland.

A modern war followed by revolutions might destroy it all over the planet. If weapons are as much improved in the next century as in the last, this will probably happen. But unless atomic energy can be tapped, which is wildly unlikely, we know that it will never be possible to box up very much more rapidly available energy in a given place than we can already box up in a high explosive shell, nor has any vapour much more poisonous than 'mustard gas' been discovered in the forty-one years that have elapsed since that substance was first produced. I think, therefore, that the odds are slightly against such a catastrophic end of civilization.

But civilization as we know it is a poor thing. And if it is to be improved there is no hope save in science. A hundred and forty years ago men, women, and children were being hanged in England for stealing any property valued at over a shilling, miners were hereditary slaves in Scotland, criminals were publicly and legally tortured to death in France. Europe was definitely rather worse off, whether in health, wealth, or morals, than the Roman Empire under Antoninus Pius in A.D. 150.

Since then we have improved very greatly in all these respects. We are far from perfect, but we live about twice as long, and we do not hang starving children for stealing food, raid the coast of Africa for slaves, or imprison debtors for life. These advances are the direct and indirect consequences of science. Physics and chemistry have made us rich, biology healthy, and the application of scientific thought to ethics by such men as Bentham has done more than any dozen saints to make us good. The process can only continue if science continues.

And pure science is a delicate plant. It has never flowered in Spain, and to-day it is almost dead in Italy. Everywhere there are strong forces working against it. Even where research is rewarded, the usual reward is a professorship with a full-time programme of teaching and administration. The bacteriologist can most easily earn a title and a fortune if he deserts research for medical practice. The potential physicist or chemist can often quadruple his income by taking up engineering or manufacture. In biology and psychology many lines of research are forbidden by law or public opinion. If science is to improve man as it has improved his environment, the experimental method must be applied to him. It is quite likely that the attempt to do so will rouse such fierce opposition that science will again be persecuted as it has been in the past.

Such a persecution may quite well be successful, especially if it is supported by religion. A world-wide religious revival, whether Christian or not, would probably succeed in suppressing experimental inquiry into the human mind, which offers the only serious hope of improving it. Again, if scientific psychology and eugenics are used as weapons by one side in a political struggle, their opponents, if successful, will stamp them out. I think that it is quite as likely as not that scientific research may ultimately be strangled in some such way as this before mankind has learnt to control its own evolution.

If so, evolution will take its course. And that course has generally been downwards. The majority of species have degenerated and become extinct, or, what is perhaps worse, gradually lost many of their functions. The ancestors of oysters and barnacles had heads. Snakes have lost their limbs and ostriches and penguins their power of flight. Man may just as easily lose his intelligence.

It is only a very few species that have developed into something higher. It is unlikely that man will do so unless he desires to and is prepared to pay the cost. If, as appears to be the case at present in Europe and North America, the less intelligent of our species continue to breed more rapidly than the able, we shall probably go the way of the dodo and the kiwi. We do not as yet know enough to avert this fate. If research continues for another two centuries, it is probable that we shall. But if, as is likely enough, the welfare of our descendants in the remote future can only be realized at a very considerable sacrifice of present happiness and liberty, it does not follow that such a sacrifice will be made.

L

It is quite likely that, after a golden age of happiness and peace, during which all the immediately available benefits of science will be realized, mankind will very gradually deteriorate.

Genius will become ever rarer, our bodies a little weaker in each generation; culture will slowly decline, and in a few thousand or a few hundred thousand years —it does not much matter which—mankind will return to barbarism, and finally become extinct.

If this happens, I venture to hope that we shall not have destroyed the rat, an animal of considerable enterprise which stands as good a chance as any other of evolving towards intelligence.

In the rather improbable event of man taking his own evolution in hand—in other words, of improving human nature, as opposed to environment — I can see no bounds at all to his progress. Less than a million years hence the average man or woman will realize all the possibilities that human life has so far shown. He or she will never know a minute's illness. He will be able to think like Newton, to write like Racine, to paint like the von Eyks, to compose like Bach. He will be as incapable of hatred as St. Francis, and when death comes at the end of a life probably measured in thousands of years he will meet it with as little fear as Captain Oates or Arnold von Winkelried. And every minute of his life will be lived with all the passion of a lover or a discoverer. We can form no idea whatever of the exceptional men of such a future.

Man will certainly attempt to leave the earth. The first voyagers into interstellar space will die, as did Lilienthal and Pilcher, Mallory and Irvine. There is no reason why their successors should not succeed in colonizing some, at least, of the other planets of our system, and ultimately the planets, if such exist, revolving round other stars than our sun. There is no theoretical limit to man's material progress but the subjection to complete conscious control of every atom and every quantum of radiation in the universe. There is, perhaps, no limit at all to his intellectual and spiritual progress.

But, whether any of these possibilities will be realized depends, as far as we can see, very largely on the events of the next few centuries. If scientific research is regarded as a useful adjunct to the army, the factory, or the hospital, and not as of all things most supremely worth doing both for its own sake and that of its results, it is probable that the decisive steps will never be taken. And unless he can control his own evolution as he is learning to control that of his domestic plants and animals, man and all his works will go down into oblivion and darkness.

THE ORIGIN OF LIFE

U NTIL about 150 years ago it was generally believed that living beings were constantly arising out of dead matter. Maggots were supposed to be generated spontaneously in decaying meat. In 1668 Redi showed that this did not happen provided insects were carefully excluded. And in 1860 Pasteur extended the proof to the bacteria which he had shown were the cause of putrefaction. It seemed fairly clear that all the living beings known to us originate from other living beings. At the same time Darwin gave a new emotional interest to the problem. It had appeared unimportant that a few worms should originate from mud. But if man was descended from worms such spontaneous generation acquired a new significance. The origin of life on the earth would have been as casual an affair as the evolution of monkeys into man. Even if the latter stages of man's history were due to natural causes, pride clung to a supernatural, or at least surprising, mode of origin for his ultimate ancestors. So it was with a sigh of relief that a good many men, whom Darwin's arguments had convinced, accepted the conclusion of Pasteur that life can originate only from life. It was possible either to suppose that life had been supernaturally created on earth some millions of years ago, or that it had been brought to earth by a meteorite or by micro-organisms floating through interstellar space. But a large number, perhaps the majority, of biologists, believed, in spite of Pasteur, that at some time in the remote past life had originated on earth from dead matter as the result of natural processes.

The more ardent materialists tried to fill in the details of this process, but without complete success. Oddly enough, the few scientific men who professed idealism agreed with them. For if one can find evidences of mind (in religious terminology the finger of God) in the most ordinary events, even those which go on in the chemical laboratory, one can without much difficulty believe in the origin of life from such processes. Pasteur's work therefore appealed most strongly to those who desired to stress the contrast between mind and matter. For a variety of obscure historical reasons, the Christian Churches have taken this latter point of view. But it should never be forgotten that the early Christians held many views which are now regarded as materialistic. They believed in the resurrection of the body, not the immortality of the soul. St. Paul seems to have attributed consciousness and will to the body. He used a phrase translated in the revised version as 'the mind of the flesh', and credited the flesh with a capacity for hatred, wrath, and other mental functions. Many modern physiologists hold similar beliefs. But, perhaps unfortunately for Christianity, the Church was captured by a group of very inferior Greek philosophers in the third and fourth centuries A.D. Since that date views as to the relation between mind and body which St. Paul, at least, did not hold, have been regarded as part of Christianity, and have retarded the progress of science.

It is hard to believe that any lapse of time will dim the glory of Pasteur's positive achievements. He published singularly few experimental results. It has even been suggested by a cynic that his entire work would not gain a Doctorate of Philosophy to-day! But every experiment was final. I have never heard of anyone who has repeated any experiment of Pasteur's with a result different from that of the master. Yet his deductions from these experiments were sometimes too sweeping. It is perhaps not quite irrelevant that he worked in his latter years with half a brain. His right cerebral hemisphere had been extensively wrecked by the bursting of an artery when he was only forty-five years old; and the united brain-power of the microbiologists who succeeded him has barely compensated for that accident. Even during his lifetime some of the conclusions which he had drawn from his experimental work were disproved. He had said that alcoholic fermentation was impossible without life. Buchner obtained it with a cell-free and dead extract of yeast. And since his death the gap between life and matter has been greatly narrowed.

When Darwin deduced the animal origin of man a search began for a 'missing link' between ourselves and the apes. When Dubois found the bones of Pithecanthropus some comparative anatomists at once proclaimed that they were of animal origin, while others were equally convinced that they were parts of a human skeleton. It is now generally recognized that either party was right, according to the definition of humanity adopted. Pithecanthropus was a creature which might legitimately be described either as a man or an ape, and its existence showed that the distinction between the two was not absolute.

Now the recent study of ultramicroscopic beings has brought up at least one parallel case, that of the bacteriophage, discovered by d'Herelle, who had been to some extent anticipated by Twort. This is the cause of a disease, or, at any rate abnormality, of bacteria. Before the size of the atom was known there was no reason to doubt that

> Big fleas have little fleas
> Upon their backs to bite 'em;
> The little ones have lesser ones,
> And so ad infinitum.

But we now know that this is impossible. Roughly speaking, from the point of view of size, the bacillus is the flea's flea, the bacteriophage the bacillus' flea; but the bacteriophage's flea would be of the dimensions of an atom, and atoms do not behave like fleas. In other words, there are only about as many atoms in a cell as cells in a man. The link between living and dead matter is therefore somewhere between a cell and an atom.

D'Herelle found that certain cultures of bacteria began to swell up and burst until all had disappeared. If such cultures were passed through a filter fine enough to keep out all bacteria, the filtrate could infect fresh bacteria, and so on indefinitely. Though the infective agents cannot be seen with a microscope, they can be counted as follows. If an active filtrate containing bacteriophage be poured over a colony of bacteria on a jelly, the bacteria will all, or almost all, disappear. If it be diluted many thousand times, a few islands of living bacteria survive for some time. If it be diluted about ten million fold, the bacteria are destroyed round only a few isolated spots, each representing a single particle of bacteriophage.

Since the bacteriophage multiplies, d'Herelle believes it to be a living organism. Bordet and others have taken an opposite view. It will survive heating and other insults which kill the large majority of organisms, and will multiply only in presence of living bacteria, though it can break up dead ones. Except perhaps in presence of bacteria, it does not use oxygen or display any other signs of life. Bordet and his school therefore regard it as a ferment which breaks up bacteria as our own digestive ferments break up our food, at the same time inducing the disintegrating bacteria to produce more of the same ferment. This is not as fantastic as it sounds, for most cells while dying liberate or activate ferments which digest themselves. But these ferments are certainly feeble when compared with the bacteriophage.

Clearly we are in doubt as to the proper criterion of life. D'Herelle says that the bacteriophage is alive, because, like the flea or the tiger, it can multiply indefinitely at the cost of living beings. His opponents say that it can multiply only as long as its food is alive, whereas the tiger certainly, and the flea probably, can live on dead products of life. They suggest that the bacteriophage is like a book or a work of art, which is constantly being copied by living beings, and is therefore only metaphorically alive, its real life being in its copiers.

The American geneticist Muller has, however, suggested an intermediate view. He compares the bacteriophage to a gene—that is to say, one of the units concerned in heredity. A fully coloured and a spotted dog differ because the latter has in each of its cells one or two of a certain gene, which we know is too small for the microscopist to see. Before a cell of a dog divides this gene divides also, so that each of the daughter-cells has one, two, or none according with the number in the parent cell. The ordinary spotted dog is healthy, but a gene common among German dogs causes a roan colour when one is present, while two make the dog nearly white, wall-eyed, and generally deaf, blind, or both. Most of such dogs die young, and the analogy to the bacteriophage is fairly close. The main difference between such a lethal gene, of which many are known, and the bacteriophage, is that the one is only known inside the cell, the other outside. In the present state of our ignorance we may regard the gene either as a tiny organism which can divide in the environment provided by the rest of the cell; or as a bit of machinery which the 'living' cell copies at each division. The truth is probably somewhere in between these two hypotheses.

Unless a living creature is a piece of dead matter plus a soul (a view which finds little support in modern biology) something of the following kind must be true. A simple organism must consist of parts A, B, C, D, and so on, each of which can multiply only in presence of all, or almost all, of the others. Among these parts are genes, and the bacteriophage is such a part which has got loose. This hypothesis becomes more plausible if we believe in the work of Hauduroy, who finds that the ultramicroscopic particles into which the bacteria have been broken up, and which pass through filters that can stop the bacteria, occasionally grow up again into bacteria after a lapse of several months. He brings evidence to show that such fragments of bacteria may cause disease, and d'Herelle and Peyre claim to have found the ultramicroscopic form of a common staphylococcus, along with bacteriophage, in cancers, and suspects that this combination may be the cause of that disease.

On this view the bacteriophage is a cog, as it were, in the wheel of a life-cycle of many bacteria. The same bacteriophage can act on different species, and is thus, so to say, a spare part which can be fitted into a number of different machines, just as a human diabetic can remain in health when provided with insulin manufactured by a pig. A great many kinds of molecule have been got from cells, and many of them are very efficient when removed from it. One can separate from yeast one of the many tools which it uses in alcoholic fermentation, an enzyme called invertase, and this will break up six times its weight of cane-sugar per second for an indefinite time without wearing out. As it does not form alcohol from the sugar, but only a sticky mixture of other sugars, its use is permitted in the United States in the manufacture of confectionery and cake-icing. But such fragments do not reproduce themselves, though they take part in the assimilation of food by the living cell. No one supposes that they are alive. The bacteriophage is a step beyond the enzyme on the road to life, but it is perhaps an exaggeration to call it fully alive. At about the same stage on the road are the viruses which cause such diseases as smallpox, herpes, and hydrophobia. They can multiply only in living tissue, and pass through filters which stop bacteria.

With these facts in mind we may, I think, legitimately speculate on the origin of life on this planet. Within a few thousand years from its origin it probably cooled down so far as to develop a fairly permanent solid crust. For a long time, however, this crust must have been above the boiling-point of water, which condensed only gradually. The primitive atmosphere probably contained little or no oxygen, for our present supply of that gas is only about enough to burn all the coal and other organic remains found below and on the earth's surface. On the other hand, almost all the carbon of these organic substances, and much of the carbon now combined in chalk, limestone, and dolomite, were in the atmosphere as carbon dioxide. Probably a good deal of the nitrogen now in the air was combined with metals as nitride in the earth's crust, so that ammonia * was constantly being formed by the action of water. The sun was perhaps slightly brighter than it is now, and as there was no oxygen in the atmosphere the chemically active ultra-violet rays from the sun were not, as they now are, mainly stopped by ozone (a modified form of oxygen) in the upper atmosphere, and by oxygen itself lower down. They penetrated to the surface of the land and sea, or at least to the clouds.

Now, when ultra-violet light acts on a mixture of water, carbon dioxide, and ammonia, a vast variety of organic substances are made, including sugars and apparently some of the materials from which proteins are built up. This fact has been demonstrated in the laboratory by Baly of Liverpool and his colleagues. In this present world such substances, if left about, decay— that is to say, they are destroyed by micro-organisms. But before the origin of life they must have accumulated till the primitive oceans reached the consistency of hot dilute soup. To-day an organism must trust to luck, skill, or strength to obtain its food. The first precursors of life found food available in considerable quantities, and had no competitors in the struggle for existence. As the primitive atmosphere contained little or no oxygen, they must have obtained the energy which they needed for growth by some other process than oxida-

* Since the above was written, ammonia has been detected spectroscopically in the atmosphere of the outer planets by Wildt.

tion—in fact, by fermentation. For, as Pasteur put it, fermentation is life without oxygen. If this was so, we should expect that high organisms like ourselves would start life as anaerobic beings, just as we start as single cells. This is the case. Embryo chicks for the first two or three days after fertilization use very little oxygen, but obtain the energy which they need for growth by fermenting sugar into lactic acid, like the bacteria which turns milk sour. So do various embryo mammals, and in all probability you and I lived mainly by fermentation during the first week of our pre-natal life. The cancer cell behaves in the same way. Warburg has shown that with its embryonic habit of unrestricted growth there goes an embryonic habit of fermentation.

The first living or half-living things were probably large molecules synthesized under the influence of the sun's radiation, and only capable of reproduction in the particularly favourable medium in which they originated. Each presumably required a variety of highly specialized molecules before it could reproduce itself, and it depended on chance for a supply of them. This is the case to-day with most viruses, including the bacteriophage, which can grow only in presence of the complicated assortment of molecules found in a living cell.

The growth and reproduction of large molecules are not, it may be remarked, quite hypothetical processes. They occur, it would seem, in certain polymerizations which are familiar to organic chemists. In my opinion the genes in the nuclei of cells still double themselves in this way. The most familiar analogy to the process is crystallization. A crystal grows if placed in a supersaturated solution, but the precise arrangement of the molecules out of several possible arrangements depends on the arrangement found in the original crystal with which the solution is 'seeded'. The metaphor of seeding, used by chemists, points to an analogy with reproduction.

The unicellular organisms, including bacteria, which were the simplest living things known a generation ago, are far more complicated. They are organisms—that is to say, systems whose parts co-operate. Each part is specialized to a particular chemical function, and prepares chemical molecules suitable for the growth of the other parts. In consequence, the cell as a whole can usually subsist on a few types of molecule, which are transformed within it into the more complex substances needed for the growth of the parts.

The cell consists of numerous half-living chemical molecules suspended in water and enclosed in an oily film. When the whole sea was a vast chemical laboratory the conditions for the formation of such films must have been relatively favourable; but for all that life may have remained in the virus stage for many millions of years before a suitable assemblage of elementary units was brought together in the first cell. There must have been many failures, but the first successful cell had plenty of food, and an immense advantage over its competitors.

It is probable that all organisms now alive are descended from one ancestor, for the following reason. Most of our structural molecules are asymmetrical, as shown by the fact that they rotate the plane of polarized light, and often form asymmetrical crystals. But of the two possible types of any such molecule, related to one another like a right and left boot, only one is found throughout living nature. The apparent exceptions to this rule are all small molecules which are not used in the building of the large structures which display the phenomena of life. There is nothing, so far as we can see, in the nature of things to prevent the existence of looking-glass organisms built from molecules which are, so to say, the mirror-images of those in our own bodies. Many of the requisite molecules have already been made in the laboratory. If life had originated independently on several occasions, such organisms would probably exist. As they do not, this event probably occurred only once, or, more probably, the descendants of the first living organism rapidly evolved far enough to over-whelm any later competitors when these arrived on the scene.

As the primitive organisms used up the foodstuffs available in the sea some of them began to perform in their own bodies the synthesis formerly performed at haphazard by the sunlight, thus ensuring a liberal supply of food. The first plants thus came into existence, living near the surface of the ocean, and making food with the aid of sunlight as do their descendants to-day. It is thought by many biologists that we animals are descended from them. Among the molecules in our own bodies are a number whose structure resembles that of chloro-phyll, the green pigment with which the plants have harnessed the sunlight to their needs. We use them for other purposes than the plants—for example, for carry-ing oxygen—and we do not, of course, know whether they are, so to speak, descendants of chlorophyll or merely cousins. But since the oxygen liberated by the first plants must have killed off most of the other organisms, the former view is the more plausible.

A number of organisms exist to-day which cannot

live in presence of oxygen. Such are the bacteria causing tetanus and gas gangrene. They may of course be descendants of air-breathers which have lost the capacity for dealing with oxygen. But I like to toy with the idea that they are the vestiges of an older order of living beings, and to think, as I examine black mud or a septic wound,

> Hic genus antiquum terrae, Titania proles,
> Fulmine deiecti fundo volvuntur in imo.

The above conclusions are speculative. They will remain so until living creatures have been synthesized in the biochemical laboratory. We are a long way from that goal. It was only this year* that Pictet for the first time made cane-sugar artificially. It is doubtful whether any enzyme has been obtained quite pure. Nevertheless I hope to live to see one made artificially. I do not think I shall behold the synthesis of anything so nearly alive as a bacteriophage or a virus, and I do not suppose that a self-contained organism will be made for centuries. Until that is done the origin of life will remain a subject for speculation. But such speculation is not idle, because it is susceptible of experimental proof or disproof.

Some people will consider it a sufficient refutation of the above theories to say that they are materialistic, and that materialism can be refuted on philosophical grounds. They are no doubt compatible with materialism, but also with other philosophical tenets. The facts are, after all, fairly plain. Just as we know of sight only in connection with a particular kind of material system called the eye, so we know only of life in connection with certain arrangements of matter, of which the biochemist

* 1928.

can give a good, but far from complete, account. The question at issue is: 'How did the first such system on this planet originate?' This is a historical problem to which I have given a very tentative answer on the not unreasonable hypothesis that a thousand million years ago matter obeyed the same laws that it does to-day.

This answer is compatible, for example, with the view that pre-existent mind or spirit can associate itself with certain kinds of matter. If so, we are left with the mystery as to why mind has so marked a preference for a particular type of colloidal organic substances. Personally I regard all attempts to describe the relation of mind to matter as rather clumsy metaphors. The bio-chemist knows no more, and no less, about this question than any one else. His ignorance disqualifies him no more than the historian or the geologist from attempting to solve a historical problem.

SOME CONSEQUENCES OF
MATERIALISM

LOOKERS-ON often see the best of a game. Materialists of a philosophical bent are commonly too occupied in argument with their opponents to draw the logical deductions from their own position. I am not myself a Materialist, but for the above reason I feel that Materialists often fail to do themselves justice. And it is futile either to deny the importance of Materialism or the large element of truth which it contains. It has been pretty completely successful in astronomy, physics, and chemistry. In biology I do not think that any facts inconsistent with it have been discovered. Nevertheless, the biologist must take cognizance of facts (such as the unity of the organism) which have not yet been fully explained on Materialistic lines, and perhaps never will be. In the field of history, both theoretical and practical, Materialism has met with a considerable measure of success in the hands of Marx, Engels, Lenin, and their disciples.

Moreover, Lenin's success as a practical historian—that is, a maker of history—has made Materialism the official creed of the Union of Socialist Soviet Republics. This body may, of course, collapse on economic grounds; but such an eventuality seems far less likely to-day than it did ten or even five years ago. Hence Materialism will probably be adopted by a large section of the human race, though most of them will presumably no more be consistent Materialists than their ancestors were consistent Christians.

I am not myself a Materialist because, if Materialism is true, it seems to me that we cannot know that it is true. If my opinions are the result of the chemical processes going on in my brain, they are determined by the laws of chemistry, not those of logic. If I believe that I am writing with real ink on real paper (for, as I write on subjects other than pure science almost entirely in railway trains, I do not use a typewriter), I have no guarantee that this is true. I can only say that the chemical processes associated with that belief increase the probable duration of my brain. And various illusions may have this effect. Unless the chemical processes associated with a belief in transubstantiation went on in the brains of my ancestors between about A.D. 1400 and 1550, these brains were liable to be rapidly oxidized at a high temperature. During the next century, however, the chemical processes associated with disbelief in transubstantiation had a similar survival value. But transubstantiation, if it was true before the Reformation, did not cease to be so on account of Luther and Calvin. To put the matter in another way, if a super-biochemist made a working model of me, atom for atom, this robot would, on a Materialistic view, have all my memories. This may be the case, but if so I do not see how knowledge is possible.

Most of the other arguments against Materialism seem to me fairly worthless. Materialists are no worse morally than other people. They need not disbelieve in morality. If matter can produce consciousness and truth as by-products, why should it not produce moral obligations? They need not be Atheists, though they generally are. But some Jews and Christians, not to speak of Edgar Allan Poe, have regarded God as a fine type of matter pervading the grosser kinds; and some Atheists, such as the late Dr. MacTaggart, have regarded all so-called material objects as mind in masquerade.

Most people's only serious objection to Materialism is simply that they find it an unpleasant idea. Obviously, however, the pleasantness of an idea is no evidence for its truth, nor *vice versa*. Many of the objections to it on this ground are, moreover, quite unfounded. For example, it is generally supposed to be incompatible with a belief in eternal life for the human individual, whereas, as a matter of fact, it probably implies eternal life, as we shall see later.

At the present time it is being attacked by physicists from two points of view. Ordinary physical observation strongly suggests that every event has a cause. But modern atomic physics does not require this principle, and it is a sound rule in science not to invoke unnecessary principles. The reason for the impasse may be illustrated by a simple case. If we have a large number of 'excited' atoms—*i.e.* atoms with more internal energy than they can keep permanently—we can show that, under given conditions, half of them will give up the extra energy within a certain time, say a thousand millionth of a second. If, for example, the excited atoms are sodium atoms, as when we throw salt into the fire, most of the extra energy comes off according to definite laws in the characteristic yellow light. But we cannot tell what an individual atom will do; we can only state the probability that it will do something within a given time. This leads to substantial certainty when we are concerned with large numbers of atoms.

For example, there are about 10^{19} (ten trillion) atoms

in a pin's head. Suppose that its physical behaviour is predicted by the laws of physics on the basis that just half the atoms in it will undergo a given process, the chance that one atom in a million will behave in an unexpected manner is rather less than the chance that a hundred thousand bridge deals running, after thorough shuffling, will give each player one suit and one only. In other words, such an event is humanly impossible, though theoretically possible.

However, Eddington, in his Gifford lectures,* has suggested the possibility that atomic indeterminism is the same thing as human free-will. In this case the brain is a device for magnifying the undetermined behaviour of atoms to an observable scale. One cannot deny such a possibility. But a biologist can make two comments on it. In the first place, the main task of biology is to explain the fact that living creatures obey laws which cannot be predicted from our present knowledge of physics. We have to explain, for example, why we tend to resemble our parents; and there are plenty of reasons less subtle than indeterminism to explain why this resemblance is not exact. In our search for new kinds of regularity in the behaviour of matter, an unexpected irregularity is a hindrance rather than a help. In the second place, the investigation of human behaviour on scientific lines makes it clear that most of our actions, and in particular most of our moral choices, are rigidly determined.

A different criticism is being urged by Sir James Jeans in a series of papers and lectures.† It is essentially

* *The Nature of the Physical World.*

† E.g. *Nature*, 1928, vol. 122, p. 689. It is also very clearly stated in his recent book, *The Universe Around Us.*

similar to Kelvin's argument about the age of the earth. But the time scale is enormously greater, since we now know that, in certain cases at least, matter can be transformed into energy. The argument runs somewhat as follows: Certain physical processes are irreversible. If we have two cylinders, one full of compressed air and one empty, and connect them, one of two things will happen. If the connection is through a suitable machine, we can make the system do some work. If it is through a tube, the pressure is soon equalized, and when this is done the system can do no more work. The process, is in fact, irreversible. Now, irreversible processes like this are going on all round us. The radiation of heat from the sun is such a process. The source of energy in the sun is probably sufficient to last another million million years or so at a satisfactory rate, but it is not infinite. The same applies to all the other sources of 'free energy' in the universe. It will ultimately 'run down' to a condition where the temperature of all parts of the universe will be the same. Most, if not all, of this energy will have been dissipated into starlight. A great deal, though very possibly not all, of its present matter, will have been transformed into starlight; and the process will be irreversible. In a general way the trend of events can be described as an increase of randomness, which is technically called entropy. If we want to diminish the entropy of one part of the universe, as when we separate the iron and oxygen of iron ore, we can do it only by a still greater increase of entropy elsewhere, as when we allow coal and oxygen to unite in a blast furnace.

Working backwards in time, we find more and more of the starlight imprisoned in the matter of stars. We can think backwards in this way for a few million

million years, but not for ever. There must have been an initial state in which the universe was, so to say, wound up, and such a state could not be reached from its present condition. Jeans provisionally equates the initial state with creation. Some unique event must be postulated (it is claimed) in the beginning of things, and he leans to a view of the universe not unlike that of the Deists, except that the breach in physical causation took place in a past remoter than our ancestors imagined. This is an unsatisfactory point of view, for, if the laws of physics were once abrogated, there is no reason why they should not be so again, and mediums and faith-healers may be defying them daily. A scientifically adequate theory of the universe must be able, in principle, to explain every state of it as due to a preceding state. It should picture it as having lasted forever, and capable of lasting forever as a going concern.

Four main lines of escape offer themselves from the argument from irreversibility to an uncaused event in the past. It has been suggested that while the stars are running down other objects—for example, gaseous nebulae—are 'running up', so that, taken as a whole, the universe has always been much as it is now. But attempts to give a physical account of the 'running up' process have generally been regarded as failures. Moreover, the present state of the universe agrees very well with the view that it is running down. Thus the stars round us are not moving at random, nor yet according to very definite rules. They behave as if they were on the way from orderly motion towards randomness. Secondly, if the universe is spatially infinite, there is a possible line of escape, for somewhere in infinity in-definitely vast sources of energy can be postulated. But there is very strong reason to believe that the universe is not infinite.

The other two lines of escape postulate a reversal of the present tendencies in the universe. At present very large aggregates of matter are impossible, because a very large star would burst as the result of its own heat production. But when the stars have cooled down their clinkers may be able to condense into larger masses. A sufficiently dense system of cold stars rotating round one another would, it is thought, be able to attract and capture vagrant starlight from outer space; for we know that radiation is attracted by matter, though rather feebly. If this is true, the dissipated energy could perhaps be collected again, and a new cycle of stellar evolution begin. I do not think that the theory of general relativity has developed far enough to make a really adequate mathematical examination of this idea possible. We do not know, in particular, whether such an event would lead to a new cycle, or merely postpone the onset of the final condition.

The fourth idea is more fantastic, but perhaps more likely to be correct. Imagine the universe to have run down, the temperature being uniform, and all other available forms of energy converted into heat. Probably most of the existing matter would have blazed away into radiation. From the point of view of normal physics, nothing more could ever happen save a blind jostling of radiation and the surviving atoms leading to no appreciable temperature differences, and no motion of large masses. This is a short-sighted view. A resting liquid at uniform temperature appears to be homogeneous, but a small microscopical particle in it is constantly being jostled by neighbouring molecules, and occasionally picks up an unusually large amount of energy and darts across the field of the microscope. Similar phenomena occur in gases near the critical point. They are called fluctuations. The probability of any but a tiny fluctuation is extremely small. Yet no fluctuation, however great, is impossible. The pin's head of which I wrote earlier might spontaneously fly to pieces, using some of its heat energy in the process. But the probability of such an event is vastly less than that of the minute deviation from normality considered earlier.

Nevertheless, the fact remains that when a steady state is reached any fluctuation, however vast, has a finite probability. Hence, if the universe is finite spatially and contains a finite amount of matter and energy, then in the course of eternity fluctuations of every possible magnitude will occur. I have made * a rough calculation from data put forward by Jeans of the time which would be needed before a run-down universe got back to a distribution as improbable as the present as the result of mere chance fluctuation. The time is about $10^{10^{100}}$ years. Perhaps this is an exaggeration, for recent work on stellar and nebular velocities suggests that the universe is not so large as I then assumed. It can, however, hardly be less than $10^{10^{80}}$ years. The number in question is altogether inconceivably vast, although a good Christian would feel himself insulted by the suggestion that his life was limited to such a period. If we wanted to write it down in decimal notation, we should require a great many times more figures than there are atoms in the universe, according to Jeans.

* *Nature*, 1928, vol. 122, p. 808.

But that number of years is just the same fraction of eternity as a second or a century. If an event occurs, on an average, every $10^{10^{100}}$ years, it has already happened an infinite number of times, and will happen an infinite number more. During all but a fraction of eternity of this order of magnitude nothing definite occurs. But on a Materialistic view there is no one to be bored by it.

At this point I should like to defend myself against a class of critics who regard such ideas as infinity and eternity as nonsensical. When I say that an event has occurred an infinite number of times I mean that with each whole number, 1, 2, 3, and so on, we can relate one past occurrence of that event which is not already related, or labelled, with another number. This is not a very difficult conception, nor does it lead to contradictions.

If this view is correct, we are here as the result of an inconceivably improbable event, and we have no right to postulate it if any less improbable hypothesis will explain our presence. If there are other stars on which intelligent beings are wondering about their origin and destiny, a far smaller and therefore vastly more probable fluctuation would be enough to account for the existence of the human race. Now, according to the theory of its birth developed by Jeans, the solar system originated from the close approach of another star to the sun, which in consequence threw out a filament that condensed into the planets. So near an approach of two stars must be very rare, but not unique. Eddington has calculated that there are probably about 100,000 other planetary systems in the universe. Quite recently, however, Jeffreys* has criticized Jeans's theory. He concludes that it would not account for the rotation of the planets. A planet which did not rotate would have only one day per year, and would probably experience such variable temperatures as to make any complicated forms of life impossible. Jeffreys thinks that in order to account for the planetary rotations another star must actually have collided with our sun. The probability of such an event is small compared with that of a tidal encounter, and on Jeffreys's theory it becomes fairly likely that our solar system, and perhaps our own planet, is the only abode of intelligent life in space. For, even if there are a few other solar systems, their planets may be unavailable for intelligent life on a variety of physical and chemical grounds. And life may originate only under very special circumstances. If this is correct, the fluctuation theory becomes plausible. We have not assumed a more improbable fluctuation than is necessary to account for our being there to marvel at its improbability. If the future progress of astronomy substantiates the uniqueness of our earth, the fluctuation theory will of course gain in likelihood.

We have seen, then, that there is no very valid reason to doubt that there will be material conditions suitable for the development of life like our own through a perhaps unimaginably small, but still finite, fraction of eternity—that is to say, through an infinite time. We do not know enough physics to say whether this means that events reoccur cyclically. If the number of possible configurations of matter and energy is finite, however large, then every configuration will occur and has occurred an infinite number of times. According to

* *The Realist*, 1928, vol. i. No. 3.

the classical physics, the number is not finite—for example, two particles may be at any distance from one another between one and two inches. But some modern developments suggest that only a finite but immense number of distances is possible.

However that may be, it appears probable that only a finite number of animal types is possible. The number is quite large. Let us consider the number of different varieties of one species of fly, *Drosophila melanogaster*, which could be made up by suitable crosses of the varieties at present in existence. There is not enough matter in all the known heavenly bodies, and probably not in the universe, to make one fly of each of the possible kinds simultaneously. The number of possible kinds of man is probably larger; the number of possible organisms less than a mile long is very much larger, but also finite. The reason for regarding the number of types as finite is as follows. Even if the number of possible configurations of living matter is infinite, a living creature acts so as to bring small disturbances in its structure back to its normal. Hence all the various possible types would be reduced by this physiological process to a number which, however large, is finite. Now, in the course of eternity any event with a finite probability must occur an infinite number of times. Hence every human type has occurred already, and will occur again. Of course, the particular kind of material structure called the human body would only be evolved in an infinitesimal fraction of those cycles in which intelligent life occurs. But the fraction would be finite, and that is all that matters.

Now, if the nature of the mind is determined by that of the body (and I think that one may hold a view substantially equivalent to this without being a full-blown Materialist), it follows that every type of human mind has existed an infinite number of times, and will do so. If, then, the mind is determined by the body, Materialism promises something hardly to be distinguished from eternal life. A mind or soul of the same properties as my own has existed during an eternal time in the past, and will exist for an eternal time in the future. Of course, this time is broken up by enormous intervals of non-existence, but it is an infinite time. Such a view differs from the theory of reincarnation in two fundamental respects. In the first place, the mind, though the same in different lives, is new each time, and does not carry over any trace of memory or experience from one to the other. Secondly, there is no reason for supposing it to exist apart from the body of which it is an aspect.

Clearly the most debatable point in the above suggestion is the assumption of identity between two minds. This follows if atoms of the same species are entirely alike except for their relations to the environment. If each one is internally unique, it is obvious that a real physics is impossible. All that we know goes to support the view that there are no internal differences. If so, two similar sets of atoms should determine minds which can be distinguished only by their relations to their surroundings. I must confess that, to me, the prospect of eternal life without memory of my present presents no overwhelming attraction. But yet, if I had the choice between death and complete loss of memory to-morrow, I should choose the latter, if it did not entail mental derangement. Most others would, I think, agree with me; so I presume that continued existence without memory is generally felt to be better than nothing. And if one regards one's personality as possessing some value, there is a certain satisfaction in the thought that in eternity it will be able to develop in all possible environments, and to express itself in all the ways possible to it. Those who have died prematurely will be able, under other conditions, to live out complete lives. Our social organization of to-day is so rudimentary that one feels justified in hoping that our present lives are very poor samples. There is no physical reason, so far as we know, why our humanity should not continue for thousands, perhaps millions, of millions of years more; and it is reasonable to hope that they will, on the whole, be happier than the present or past ages.

If, however, evolution continues, it is likely that in most of our past and future lives you and I have been or will be relatively feeble-minded throwbacks among a more perfect humanity. If so, we shall probably be quite well treated. It is a consoling thought that, even if humanity lasts a million million years and devotes itself entirely to science and mathematics, there will be plenty of quite simple problems still unsolved. For example, there will not have been time and space enough to breed one each of all the theoretically possible varieties of *Drosophila melanogaster*, or to synthetize all the possible organic molecules of a molecular weight less than 10,000. So that I, at least, could find congenial occupations in a world of supermen.

A corollary of the above ideas is that every two persons who meet in the present life have a finite possibility of meeting again, and will therefore do so an infinite number of times, in each case to be parted once more. I believe that they are a logical deduction from thoroughgoing Materialism; and to my own mind the most surprising thing about them is that they have not, to my knowledge, been made before. They are independent of the precise type of Materialism adopted. I have taken the word in its widest sense, to denote the view that all occurrences depend on phenomena obeying definite mathematical laws, which it is the business of physics to discover. It is quite unimportant whether we call our ultimate reality matter, electric charge, ψ-waves, mind-stuff, neutral stuff, or what not, provided that it obeys laws which can, in principle, be formulated mathematically.

While I think that the theory here put forward is the only logical outcome of Materialism, it may yet have a certain cogency for those who are not Materialists. Though an Agnostic, I am personally much attracted by a modified Hegelian view which regards mind as absolute, and finite minds as contingent, their actual behaviour being regulated by laws of the same general type as regulate other phenomena. On such a view there is nothing unique or permanent about the finite mind, and it may be expected to recur under suitable conditions. Nor is there any reason to doubt that the phenomenal world is eternal. Clearly, however, on such a hypothesis I cannot have so sure and certain a hope of eternal life as if I were a consistent Materialist! The only people who can take no interest in the possibilities which I have suggested are those who regard their souls as absolutely unique and individual. If Christianity is true, they will probably spend eternity in hell (many are called, but few are chosen). According to Buddhism, they have to look forward to a vast number of reincarnations, all, on a balance, unhappy. Some modern creeds purport to be more hopeful. Spiritualists speak of a bright future; but, to judge from such communications as I have received from 'spirits', the average spirit is a rather unpleasant type of imbecile. As for those who do not accept any revelation, it is hard to see what reasons they have to expect anything but annihilation. If, however, I am a natural phenomenon, I see no reason why I should not recur like other natural phenomena.

The speculation put forward in this essay will appear strange. I claim that it is a rational speculation. It is put forward for criticism on rational grounds. I can only add that it grew in my mind during an honest endeavour to shape a view of the universe, and in particular of its remote past and future, which would be consistent with modern physical theory. At the same time, as a geneticist, I was studying the facts available as to the determination of human personality, and it appeared to me as a probable deduction from them that the number of possible personalities, though very large, is finite. If this is the case, and material conditions suitable for life have an infinite duration in time, the other conclusions seem to follow. If they are true, the universe is slightly, but not perhaps very much, better from the human point of view than had previously appeared.

GOD-MAKERS

I AM fond of honorific titles, and I think that life has lost slightly in picturesqueness by their obsolescence. Besides his Majesty the King, his Holiness the Pope, and his Worship the Mayor, I should like to be able to speak of his Ferocity the Major-General, his Velocity the Air-Marshal, and his Impiety the President of the Rationalist Press Association. Nevertheless, the most magnificent of all such titles belongs to a past which is not likely to be revived. It occurs in an inscription erected near Dratch in honour of the Roman emperors Diocletian and Maximian, who are described as 'Diis genitis et deorum creatoribus'—that is to say, 'Begotten by gods and creators of gods'. In those happy days the path to divinity was easier than in our irreligious age. A claim to divine descent might be made on somewhat slender grounds; but, as Diocletian and Maximian named their successors, who, unless deposed during their lifetime, automatically became gods on dying, they could quite legitimately be claimed as god-makers.

It is only when we remember that they were first promulgated in an age of easy deification that we can properly assess the Christian dogmas of the divinity of Christ and the semi-divinity of Mary. At that time there was nothing in such assertions to surprise their pagan hearers, though unbelieving Jews might take a different view; and, as a God, Christ was clearly an improvement on Claudius or Hadrian. But if Christianity was probably the best of a number of competing creeds, it was

also the product of an age when the moral and intellectual levels of the group of humanity round the
Mediterranean were low—a fact sufficiently attested by
their habit of indiscriminate god-making.

The saints, who perform so many of the minor functions of divinity in the Catholic scheme, are rather a
mixed lot. Some men and women have achieved sanctity
by virtue, others by hypocrisy, some again by sheer luck.
Of this latter goodly fellowship none stand higher than
St. Protasus and St. Gervaise. These worthy men (or
possibly women, for, as we shall see, less is known about
them than one might suppose) lived in northern Italy
in late palaeolithic times, some ten to thirty thousand
years ago, and died after doubtless unusually blameless
lives. We do not know whether their beliefs on un-
ascertainable matters were so coherent as to be dignified
by the name of a religion. But they, or at least those
who buried them, can hardly have believed that death
was the end of Man's individual existence. For they
took a great deal of trouble with corpses. First, the flesh
was removed from the bones. They may have allowed it
to decay, and have dug the skeleton up again after the
lapse of some time. It is also possible that they stripped
it from the bones soon after death. In this case it was
probably eaten, at least in part, the meal being of a
sacramental character, as still with some primitive
peoples. If so, perhaps we must credit the eaters with
religion of a kind, for the simple and materialistic belief
that you can enter into communion with another person
by eating him is at the basis of the most powerful
religion of to-day.

The skeletons underwent a further treatment. Their
heads were removed, and then the various bones were

N

smeared with red ochre. We do not know the reasons for the first operation. Perhaps it was done to prevent the ghosts of the dead from walking. The meaning of the second is more obvious. The blood, as Holy Writ informs us, is the life. So, for a future life future blood is necessary. Ochre is a very good substitute for blood. It is red, and, not being susceptible of decay, may serve as a respiratory pigment during an eternal life. Moreover, recent biochemical research has demonstrated its peculiar suitability as a catalyst for those oxidations which are perhaps even more important in the future life than the present one. For spirit means breath, and the essential function of breathing is to supply oxygen.

Like the owners of other skeletons similarly fortified with red ochre (and many such have been found round Milan), the souls of Gervaise and Protasus, we may believe, chased the aurochs and the wild horse across the happy hunting-grounds, and tracked the woolly rhinoceros to his lair in the Elysian swamps. But faith can work miracles, even on a woolly rhinoceros. Just as it can turn water into wine, and wine into blood (in spite of the fact that oenin, the pigment of grapeskins, unlike chlorophyll, that of leaves, stands in no chemical relationship to haemoglobin), so it can convert a woolly rhinoceros into a dragon. For in the town hall at Klagenfurt, in Carinthia, stands, or stood till recently, the skull of a woolly rhinoceros. To be more precise, the infidel palaeontologist would assign it to *Rhinoceros tichorinus*; but the noble knight who slew the dire monster in question said it was a dragon, and he ought to have known. Perhaps he really did kill the last survivor of this species. But more probably it had been extinct for some thousands of years, in which case it is not inconceivable that one of his villeins dug up the skull in his back garden.

Now, if the faith of a quite ordinary knight can transform a woolly rhinoceros into a dragon, why should not that of a particularly holy bishop convert two of its hunters into saints? At any rate, it did so. For a hundred centuries or more the spirits of Gervaise and Protasus hunted their ghostly quarry. But one day their pleasant, if monotonous, existence was sharply interrupted. Two angels appeared, and bore them away, perhaps slightly protesting, to the Christian heaven, where their spears were exchanged for harps and their skins for crowns. As they almost instantly began to work miracles in response to the prayers of the faithful, it appears that they must have adapted themselves to their new conditions more rapidly than might have been expected. Of course, several other cases have been recorded in which souls have gone to an apparently inappropriate heaven. Such were the souls of the penguins whose baptism by the myopic St. Maël is reported by Anatole France, and that of the Christian knight Donander, which, as Cabell tells us in that most indecent, blasphemous, and amusing book *The Silver Stallion*, was transported to Valhalla by an unfortunate oversight, and subsequently elevated to Asgard on physiological grounds. And in our own days a respectable German medical officer of health has found himself in the Shinto heaven with Amaterasu and the divine Emperors. Robert Koch, the discoverer of the tubercle and cholera bacilli, and the joint founder with Pasteur of bacteriology, is worshipped as a god in at least one Japanese laboratory. It must at once be admitted that he appears to be quite an efficient god. Japan has produced a number of really excellent bacteriologists. But perhaps in another fifty years bacteriology may no longer be as important in medicine as it is now, and the divine Koch, like older gods, may prove a hindrance to medical progress by diverting effort into ineffective channels.

Spiritual events often have material causes, and we must now trace the mundane events which enriched heaven with its only palaeolithic saints. St. Ambrose was one of the first batch of well-born Romans who, after its establishment as the State religion, entered the ministry of the Christian Church as a career. Like myself, he was unbaptized at the age of thirty-four; but, unlike me, he became a bishop before the application of that sacrament. He was not only a very able statesman, but a good poet—one of the pioneers of rhyming verse in Latin. In the year A.D. 385 he came into conflict with the secular authorities. The Dowager Empress Justina was an Arian, and demanded the use of a church in Milan for her co-religionists. The history of her conflict with Ambrose has been told by Gibbon in his twenty-seventh chapter. I shall not attempt to tell it again in detail.

Ambrose's tactics resembled those of Mr. Gandhi to-day. While comparing the Empress to Jezebel and Herodias, he affected to deplore the rioting to which his language inevitably led. His methods were successful. The imperial court left Milan, and promulgated an edict of toleration for Arianism. The saint's protest against this tyrannical law led to a sentence of banishment. He blockaded himself in the cathedral with a pious body-guard, including Augustine's mother, who kept up their spirits by singing his newly invented rhyming hymns, which brought frequent tears to the eyes of the future Saint Augustine, who had recently been baptized.

During the siege, in response to a vision, he dug for the bones of Gervaise and Protasus. They were found under a church floor, and it was revealed to St. Ambrose that they had suffered martyrdom as Christians under Nero. The multitude were impressed not only by the miraculous freshness of the respiratory pigment of the martyrs, but by the large size of their bones. The Cro-Magnon race, to which the martyrs probably belonged, were, of course, very tall. The bones were carried with due pomp to the Ambrosian basilica. On the way a number of demons were expelled from lunatics, and a man called Severus, who had been blind for some years, was cured on touching the bier of the saints. St. Augustine was in Milan at the time, and records these miracles, which were entirely successful in reinforcing the effect of the hymns. The soldiers did not dare to risk the bloodshed which would have been necessary to effect the capture of St. Ambrose. Shortly afterwards the edict of toleration in favour of the Arians was withdrawn, and the illustrious examples of Gervaise and Protasus did much to confirm the general belief in the efficacy of relics. It only remains to add that twenty-four years after the discovery of the palaeolithic saints Rome was sacked by the Arian Goths. This time the trinitarian saints were unable to rise to the occasion. Alaric was made of different stuff from Justina.

But saints are, after all, not gods; and a similar story, though involving a different red pigment, comes down to us from an age nearer to our own. At the Last Supper Jesus is reported to have said of the bread and wine: 'Take, eat; this is my body', and 'This is my blood of the new testament, which is shed for many'.

Personally, I am not one of those who find it probable

that Jesus is a mainly mythical figure. A large number of his sayings seem to me to cohere as expressions of a definite and quite human character, which could hardly have been invented by disciples who wished to prove his divinity. He used figurative language about himself, calling himself, for example, the door and the vine. His self-identification with bread and wine is on a par with these utterances. But by a more or less fortuitous chain of events it has been taken much more seriously. One can imagine developments of Christianity in which every church door or every vine was identified with Jesus, as a pious Hindu may identify every cow with Agni. The actual form of the transubstantiation dogma appears to be due to three facts—the type of mystery religion flourishing in the early days of Christianity, the peculiarities of Latin and Greek grammar, and the activities of a particular god-making bacillus, which, besides upholding the views of the Angelic Doctor, St. Thomas Aquinas, founded a college at each of our two older universities.

The importance of sacramental meals in mystery religions has been sufficiently stressed by others. If to-day we find it difficult to imagine how so much emotion could gather round the act of eating, we must remember that the majority of the early Christians were so poor as to have first-hand experience of real hunger. To most of them food must have presented itself not as a source of mildly pleasant sensations, but vividly as a life-giver.

Once Jesus had been identified with the sacramental meal, it was inevitable that some theory of that identity should be developed. The philosophers got busy. The only tools of philosophers, until very recently, were words, and the art of using words correctly was called 'logic'. In fact, words are well adapted for description and the arousing of emotion, but for many kinds of precise thought other symbols are much better. Russell and Whitehead were perhaps the first philosophers to take this fact seriously. But a perusal of their books makes it clear that even a greatly improved symbolism leaves room for a very comprehensive disagreement on fundamental tenets.

The European languages are characterized by a highly developed system of adjectives. For example, an Arab, instead of describing the Board of the R.P.A. as infidel men, would call them fathers of infidelity; and I gather that a Chinese might also avoid the use of an adjective in a somewhat untranslatable manner. Now, the philosophy of the Middle Ages was the work of men who were ignorant of nature, but learned in Latin grammar. Neglecting the verbs, they tried to describe the universe in terms of substantives and adjectives, to which they attributed an independent existence under the names of substances and accidents or attributes. Modern physicists are engaged in a somewhat similar attempt to describe it in terms of verbs only, their favourite verb at the moment being to undulate, or wiggle. They are not concerned with what wiggles.

The scholastic philosophy, like any other, led to results calculated to alarm the pious. The soul was in danger of becoming a mere adjective of the body, and was therefore relegated to a special category of 'substantial forms', thus rendering it sufficiently durable to withstand eternal punishment. With such highly developed attributes, substance might have disappeared altogether had not a place been found for it by the genius of St. Thomas Aquinas. St. Thomas, it is said, was one of the fattest men who ever lived, and in his latter years could carry out the ritual of the Mass only at a specially constructed concave altar. Hence his capacity for levitation was even more miraculous than that of lighter saints. In spite of the distance which separated him, in middle age, from the consecrated elements, he was able to observe that no perceptible change occurred when the bread and wine were converted into the body and blood of Christ. Very well, said he, in an excellent hymn, most inadequately rendered in the English hymn-book: 'Praestet fides supplementum sensuum defectui' (Let faith supplement the deficiency of the senses). It did. At the critical moment the substance of the bread and wine was converted into God; but, as all the accidents were unaltered, no perceptible difference occurred. Fortunately, he did not draw the full consequences from his theory. For, if no one could notice the difference when a piece of bread is converted into God, it would appear that the converse operation might also be imperceptible, and no one would notice any change if the object of St. Thomas's worship were converted into a wafer or some other inanimate object. It is also interesting to note that, while St. Thomas was a realist about things in general, he anticipated the views of Bishop Berkeley when it came to the consecrated elements. For he believed that their sensible qualities were directly caused and supported by the deity latent in them.

Now, the dogma of transubstantiation, which needed such strange intellectual props, was not merely based, like many theological dogmas, on traditions of past events which had been brooded over by successive generations of the pious. It was grounded on a series of very well-attested miracles. Not only had individual ecstatics seen visions of Jesus in the host, but large numbers of people had seen hosts bleeding. The first of such events which is known to me occurred in England about A.D. 900, in the presence of Archbishop Odo. Among the most famous is the miracle of Bolsena (also known as the miracle of the Bloody Corporal), which is portrayed in Raphael's well-known picture, and converted a priest who doubted transubstantiation. Allowing for a certain amount of exaggeration for the glory of God, I see no reason to disbelieve in these miracles. Their nature becomes very probable from the way in which they tended to occur in series, especially in Belgium. A 'bleeding host' appeared in a certain church. The faithful went to adore it, and fairly soon others appeared in the vicinity. There is very strong reason to suppose that we have to deal with an outbreak of infection of bread by *Bacillus prodigiosus* (the miraculous bacillus), which would naturally be spread by human contacts. Their organism grows readily on bread, and produces red patches, which the eye of faith might well take for blood.

The miracle of Bolsena appears to have finally converted Pope Urban IV. to the views, not only of St. Thomas, but of his contemporary, St. Juliana of Liége, one of the two women who have initiated important changes in Catholic practice, the other being St. Marie Marguerite Alacocque, the initiator of the cult of the Sacred Heart. St. Juliana had a vision of the moon with a black spot on it, and was told that the moon signified the Church, the spot being the absence of a special cult of Christ's body. As a result of this vision the Bishop of Liége instituted the feast of Corpus Christi, and in 1264 Pope Urban IV., who had been Archdeacon of Liége, made its celebration compulsory throughout Western Europe. The office for the feast was written by St. Thomas Aquinas. In honour of Christ's body a college was founded at Cambridge within the next century, though the corresponding establishment at Oxford dates back only to shortly before the Reformation. There is no record of what St. Juliana said to the angel who told her about the activities of the poet Kit Marlowe, student of Corpus Christi College, Cambridge. For it appears from the record of his 'damnable opinion' that he was a remarkably militant Rationalist, while a spy stated that he was 'able to shewe more sound reasons for Atheisme than any devine in Englande is able to geve to prove devinitie'. Perhaps, however, such things are kept from the ears of the blessed.

Unfortunately, *Bacillus prodigiosus* did not confine its efforts to inspiring queer metaphysics and founding colleges. If a bleeding host was God's body, any bit of bread which appeared to bleed was a host, presumably stolen and desecrated. Throughout the ages of faith the same incidents re-occurred. A piece of bread in a house started to 'bleed'. An informer, generally a servant, went to the authorities. The family were tortured, and finally confessed to having stolen or bought a consecrated wafer and run daggers through it. They were then generally burned alive. Such an incident was often a signal for a massacre of Jews, as in the pogrom of 1370, commemorated in the disgusting stained-glass windows of the cathedral of Ste. Gudule at Brussels, and in the French outbreaks of 1290 and 1433. Sometimes the victims were Gentiles, as in the case recorded by Paolo Uccello in a series of panels which were on view at the London exhibition of Italian painting in

1930. Doubtless among them were a few fools who were genuinely celebrating black masses; but the emphasis laid on the blood in contemporary accounts seems to incriminate *Bacillus prodigiosus*. In England the belief in transubstantiation ceased abruptly in the sixteenth century to be part of the law of the land. 'Hoc est corpus' became *hocus pocus*. But in France the attempt to make injuries to consecrated wafers a capital offence, as deicide, was one of the causes of the revolution of 1830.

So much for *Bacillus prodigiosus*, an organism which produced a delusion more serious than many diseases. But this god-making tendency seems to be one of the more unfortunate vices to which the human intellect is subject. We cannot observe a remarkable phenomenon without postulating something behind it. So far, so good; but we then proceed, if we are not careful, to endow that something with a personality, and deduce the oddest ethical implications—for example, that it is wrong to stick knives through certain pieces of bread. The same tendency operates in the sphere of science. A generalization is made from certain facts, and called a Law of Nature. This is then supposed to acquire, in some quite unexplained way, an ethical value, and to become a norm for conduct. Thus Darwin stated, probably quite correctly, that evolution had been mainly due to natural selection—*i.e.* the elimination of certain individuals, called the unfit, in each generation. The obvious comment was: 'So much the worse for nature; let us try to control our own evolution in some other way'. But a number of theorists, including even a few second-rate biologists, seem to have regarded it as an excuse for imitating nature. The weak, it was said, should be eliminated in various ways, and various forms of internecine struggle, from war to economic competition, were justified by an appeal to nature, which was only justifiable if nature represented God's unalterable plan —a view which these writers did not generally hold. The fact that in most civilized communities the poor breed more quickly than the rich shows that, from a Darwinian point of view, the poor are on the whole fit and the rich unfit. To call the rapidly breeding sections of the community unfit is certainly bad Darwinism. They may be undesirable, but that is another matter. To attempt to suppress them in the name of Darwinism is an example of muddled thinking arising out of a partial deification of a law of nature.

Is the god-making tendency ineradicable, or may we hope that it will gradually die out or be sublimated into other channels? As long as it goes on there is very little chance for the development of a rational ethic based on the observable consequences of our actions. To answer this question one must consider the most important grounds for Atheism. Perhaps the simplest hypothesis about the universe is that it has been designed by an almighty and intelligent creator. Darwin showed that much of the apparent design could be explained otherwise; but there still remains a group of facts, such as those collected by L. J. Henderson in *The Fitness of the Environment*, which are at present more readily conformable with the design theory than with any other. It is on the ethical side that Theism has broken down most completely. For an almighty and all-knowing creator cannot also be all-good. It has only been possible to believe in all-powerful gods by attributing to them one or more of the seven deadly sins. The Graeco-Roman gods were at first conceived of as sharing all man's moral infirmities. Later, as their characters were idealized, their failure to improve matters here below was attributed to what was essentially sloth rather than active cruelty.

With Christianity the Deity became more actively interested in human affairs, and it was necessary to attribute to him the darker defects of pride and wrath. His pride was particularly offended by the attempts of Satan and Adam to become like him, and his wrath visited the sin of the latter upon his descendants during thousands of years. A robust spirit like Thomas Paine could still see justice in the universe. It is to more delicate minds like that of Shelley that we look for the development of Atheism on ethical grounds. The turning-point came perhaps when, under the influence of the Utilitarians, the State set itself to be less cruel than nature or the hell-filling god of the clergy. We do not condemn our worst criminals to anything as bad as an inoperable cancer involving a nerve trunk. Dartmoor, our nearest equivalent to hell, has its alleviations, and, what is more, a hope of ultimate release. It became impossible to believe that the creator of the universe, even of a universe which did not include hell, was worthy of our moral admiration.

Christianity had, of course, attempted to meet such a criticism by the doctrine that God had become a man and suffered with men. This defence is based on the celebrated hypothesis that two blacks make a white, known to moralists as the retributive theory of punishment. The theory that a wrong act deserves the infliction of suffering is part of Christian ethics, and is responsible for any amount of cruelty even to-day. And the participation of God in human suffering, while admirable in a finite deity like Heracles, does not absolve an almighty power from the blame of having created suffering humanity.

Our present-day Theists generally find two ways out of the dilemma. Either suffering is needed to perfect human character, or God is not almighty. The former theory is disproved by the fact that some people who have suffered very little, but have been fortunate in their ancestry and education, have very fine characters. The objection to the second is that it is only in connection with the universe as a whole that there is any intellectual gap to be filled by the postulation of a deity. And a creator could presumably create whatever he or it wanted. The evolution of life on earth can be pretty satisfactorily explained if we make certain assumptions about matter and life. The origin of the heavenly bodies presents greater difficulties, as will be apparent to any reader of Jeans's *The Universe Around Us*. The theory of creation is essentially a refusal to think back beyond a certain time in the past when it becomes difficult to follow the chain of causation. To hold such a belief is, therefore, always an excuse for intellectual laziness, and generally a sign of it. Probably we are waiting for a new Darwin to explain stellar evolution. But meanwhile an almighty deity would at least explain the apparent irreversibility of natural processes, while a finite deity struggling against the imperfections of matter would explain nothing whatever; and I know of no scientific facts which point to such a hypothesis. Humanity, or any other aggregate of such a kind, may very well take the place of god in an ethical system, but is not a god in any intelligible sense of that term.

Hence, so long as, on the one hand, scientific knowledge is preserved and expanded, and on the other man keeps his ethical standards above those of nature, the prospects for god-makers are by no means as rosy as they were in the past. I do not, however, think that the only alternatives to Theism are Agnosticism or any of the various forms of Materialism, even though I should call myself an Agnostic if forced to classify myself. There is a great deal of evidence that the universe as a whole possesses certain characters in common with the human mind. The Materialist can agree with this statement, as he regards the mind as a special aspect of one small fraction of the universe in physical relation with the rest. The idealist regards our knowledge of mind as knowledge from inside, and therefore more satisfactory than our knowledge of matter. Unfortunately, there is a tendency to identify the absolute—*i.e.* the universe considered in its mind-like aspect—as in some sort an equivalent of God. I cannot see the cogency of this view. The absolute is not a creator, nor a soul animating otherwise inert matter, but just the universe looked at from the most comprehensive possible point of view. It cannot be identified with any of its constituents, though in the opinion of absolute idealists the human mind is more like it than is any other known finite existent.

Such a philosophy does, as a matter of fact, supply a fairly satisfactory emotional substitute for Theism. It leads one to feel at home in the universe, and yet does not lend itself readily to the attribution of supernatural qualities to finite objects or finite events, which is the essence of all religions. Unfortunately, the history of Hinduism shows that it is compatible with religion in some of its least savoury forms. Brahma is the absolute; but, though he, or it, is venerated, he is not the centre of any important cult. Worship is reserved for Vishnu, Siva, and other minor gods and goddesses. For god-making has been carried out on a very large scale in India. But Brahma at least offers the philosophical Hindu an opportunity of 'turning his back on heaven', while preserving his piety—a gesture impossible to a European.

If this be taken as a condemnation of absolute ideal-ism, it should be noted that in Spiritualism we have the beginnings of a new religion, which can exist quite apart from any belief in a supreme deity, and often does so on the continent of Europe, though British and American Spiritualists generally preserve a more or less Christian background. Clearly Spiritualism demands scientific in-vestigation, which would disclose remarkable facts—possibly of the type in which Spiritualists believe—more probably concerning the psychology of small groups. As things are, the Spiritualists are engaged in the same early stages of god-making as the primitive races, who are still mainly animists and ancestor wor-shippers. Unless the process is checked, Spiritualism will presumably evolve into a fully developed religion, with sacred objects, intolerance, and that vast diversion of effort into fruitless channels which is in some ways the most characteristic feature of the religions.

I notice among many of my Rationalist friends a lack of interest in the history of religions, which is quite natural when one has examined their fully developed forms and found them unsatisfactory. Nevertheless, the god-making tendency is always with us, and only by a study of its past are we likely to be able to curb its development in the present.

PHYSICS
DECLARES ITS INDEPENDENCE

SOME years ago Huxley defined science as organized common sense. This definition is valid enough in the early stage of scientific development, but a period is fairly soon reached when common sense no longer suffices. Thus in mathematics negative and complex numbers, which so greatly offend the common sense of the schoolboy, formed the thin edge of the wedge, and to-day mathematicians are prepared to deal with 'quantities' that do not obey the ordinary rules of arithmetic, and manifolds which have hardly any of the properties of space. The results obtained when voyaging in these strange seas of thought turn out in many cases, however, to be applicable to the ordinary affairs of life. Nevertheless, modern mathematicians say that they are not engaged in investigating reality, but in working out the necessary consequences of hypotheses for whose truth they do not vouch.

Common-sense physics deals with material objects occupying a definite space, which can be moved by pulling or pushing, and common sense is happier with pushing than pulling. For a long time the progress of physics favoured this common-sense interpretation. Thus, suction was shown to depend on pushing by the air, heat to be a mode of motion, gases and even electricity to be composed of minute apparently impenetrable particles, and so on. Nevertheless, even in the seventeenth century common sense was beginning to be found wanting. Newton was compelled in practice to admit that only relative motion mattered in physics, although he clung theoretically to the ideas of absolute rest and motion. And in spite of various efforts to escape from such a conclusion, gravitation had to be interpreted as the action of matter at a distance. In the nineteenth century the odder properties of material systems came more and more to be attributed to the ether, a substance supposed to exist in otherwise empty space, and credited with the transmission of electric and magnetic forces, and of light and other radiations. But the atoms of matter were supposed to possess the same kinds of properties as the familiar material objects of everyday life.

Towards the end of the nineteenth century this position began to show weakness in two directions. The ether was displaying properties which seemed to be mutually contradictory; in particular it behaved as if it were at rest with regard to moving objects, yet gave no signs of streaming in between them. And the atom was showing less and less resemblance to a little billiard ball.

In the twentieth century the contradictory behaviour of the ether led Einstein to enunciate the theory of relativity. Perhaps the simplest way to understand the difficulties which it solves is as follows. Material systems have optical and mechanical properties. These generally agree. When they do not agree, at first sight we trust the mechanical properties. Thus we say that an image is not really behind a mirror, a stick is not really bent when put into water, and so on. Allowing for such properties of light as reflection and refraction, we can fit matter and light into the same framework of common-sense space and time, so long as we only consider bodies intermediate in size between a molecule and a planet, and not in relative motion faster than a few miles per minute. So common-sense space and time are quite good enough for all ordinary purposes.

When, however, we go outside these limits, and consider bodies as small as an atom or as large as the sun, or moving with such speeds as the stars in their courses, their optical and mechanical properties refuse to fit together unless we modify our conceptions of space and time. The mechanics of rapidly moving bodies, such as the planet Mercury, also become more self-consistent when this is done. Some of the qualitative results of the theory of relativity are fairly simple. If we consider two events occupying a time and space small compared with those separating them, the interval between them can be separated into years and miles according to different schemes, each appropriate to different observers. Thus the signing of the confederation of the German Empire and that of the Treaty of Versailles occurred, according to the geometry and time scale appropriate to the earth, in the same place at an interval of forty-eight years. Now, suppose a star to be passing the earth with half the velocity of light, there would be a common-sense geometry and time scale appropriate to events on that star, whether there were intelligent observers on it or not. Only in terms of that geometry could events on the star be described at all simply. In terms of the star's time and space frame the two treaties would have been framed at places twenty-eight light-years apart at a time-interval of fifty-five years. Similarly two events which in the earth's common-sense space and time scales are simultaneous, say, the coronation of Charlemagne and the explosion of the star in Aquila which was seen on the earth in 1918, would be centuries apart in time, and even further apart in space than they appear to us, in the common-sense geometry and time of the moving star. Common-sense space and time are not illusions. They are conveniences, but they do not give as full or impartial an account of the relations between events as the space-time of the theory of relativity, and physicists can attain greater accuracy by using the latter.

Kant's criticism of our ideas of space and time was fundamental for philosophy but quite sterile for physics, because Kant himself had nothing definite to put in their place, as Einstein has done. Similarly the philosophical criticisms of the ideas of matter have been of no value to physicists, though they were valuable in allowing biology, ethics, and other branches of thought to grow up without too much respect for physical theory, which was generally over-simplified.

But in 1927 Heisenberg introduced into physics as a quantitative principle the fact that we cannot observe an object without altering it, a principle which in philosophy was held by extreme idealists. The fact to be explained was that atoms do not take out or give up energy gradually, like large moving bodies, but in finite packets, or quanta. As any observation, for example, by means of light, involves the taking out or giving up of at least a quantum of energy, the quantum gives a limit to the possible accuracy of observation. We cannot determine accurately both where a particle is and how fast it is going, and the quantum is our unit of uncertainty. There is thus a connection between atomicity and the fact that phenomena are observed; on the other hand, electrons and other units of matter are not anywhere particular on going at any particular speed. In other words, the connection between matter and space and time is not as close as common sense holds. Such is the world view of Heisenberg and his followers.

Many physicists attempt to avoid these conclusions by adopting de Broglie and Schrödinger's wave mechanics. On this hypothesis moving particles, like light rays, are merely the expression on moving trains of waves. Certain wave configurations alone are possible, and quantum phenomena occur for the same kind of reason that a vibrating violin string must have one, two, three, or some whole number of nodes, but cannot have a fractional number. For the pulling or pushing of ordinary mechanisms are substituted such subtler forms of interaction as the interference of wave trains, producing stationary or moving beats. Whether even by such concessions it will be possible to retain the notion that an event occurs at a definite place and time is still an open question. Many physicists doubt it.

In any case physics is only able to explain and predict observable phenomena on the basis of a theory more removed from our ordinary ideas than the philosophy of Hegel or the mythology of the Arabian Nights. This theory (for the mathematical consequences of the theories of Heisenberg and Schrödinger are so far identical) is not materialistic in the sense of explaining the world in terms of 'common-sense' matter, but still less is it biological or spiritual, even though there may be room in it for a radical indeterminism, the predictable behaviour of large bodies being merely a statistical result of the averaging of the unpredictable conduct of individual atoms.

Whatever may be its subsequent development, it is clear that in future physics will be based on its own notions. Biology has not yet reached a stage where any of its results contradict the laws of physics, though of course they are not all explicable on physical grounds at present. Only time can show whether the investigation of such material systems as our own bodies will reveal in matter subtleties of behaviour beyond the reach of the physicist's methods, or whether the study of the atom will be sufficient to explain the phenomena of life. But the new developments of physics certainly seem to bring nearer the day when science will be a single whole, revealing a world immeasurably more complicated and beautiful than imagination or adventurous reason could picture without the aid of scientific method.

SCIENCE AND INVENTION

THE uneducated man or woman does not distinguish clearly between science and invention, and lumps together Marconi or Burbank, whose work was wholly directed to practical ends, and Rutherford or Morgan, who are out to discover principles without much regard for their practical utility. The half-educated realize the difference between the two a little too clearly. For while some pure scientists devote themselves wholly to theory and observation, others are as great inventors as their colleagues in the realm of applied science. And the practical inventor occasionally produces a machine which revolutionizes the theory as well as the practice of pure science.

Within the realm of pure science inventions are almost always made in order to enable some phenomenon previously imperceptible, unmeasurable, or only theoretically possible, to be observed. And hence, of the laboratory inventions which have, so to speak, escaped into the outside world, some of the greatest are methods of observation. Whether or not he invented that instrument, Galileo certainly made the first practical telescope for the purpose of observing the stars, and applied it to the discovery of Jupiter's satellites and Venus' crescent disc, not to navigation, war, or sport. But his instrument was the parent, not only of the giant astronomical telescopes of to-day, but of the sailor's telescope, the binoculars of the theatre-goer and racing man, and the telescopic sights of the soldier and the big-game hunter.

The physiological laboratory of the Collège de France in Paris has been the nursery of two inventions which have ministered to human pleasure, the cinematograph and the artificial breeding of oysters. The latter was probably made with practical ends in view, but the former was at first developed by Marey simply as a means for studying human and animal movement. Marey, who was a professor of physiology, was the first person to take a series of photographs of a moving animal or man with the same camera. At first they were taken on a plate, not a film, and he was much more interested in finding out how a horse's legs moved when galloping, than in projecting his photographs. So, though he began his work in 1870 it was not till 1889 that the first series of photographs were satisfactorily thrown upon a screen by Evans and Friese-Greene.

The principle that a series of slightly different pictures give the illusion of movement was discovered in 1829 by Plateau, another physiologist. He was interested in the persistence of visual images, and while investigating after-images of the sun he looked at it for too long, and went blind. He occupied his blindness, which was only temporary, by inventing a toy called the phenakistoscope, in which a series of pictures like those of the well-known Mickey Mouse gave an impression of continuous motion. But in 1848, while Professor of Physics at Ghent, he became permanently blind, so though he lived till 1889, he never saw a cinematograph.

As a Utopian dreamer, I like to toy with the idea that in some year the cinematograph theatres of the world will contribute one part in a million of their takings to the proper endowment of the laboratories of Marey and

Plateau, and that Hollywood will honour them with statues.

Many of our familiar instruments were developed for purposes of scientific research very different from those for which they are now used. The barometer, as its name implies, was originally a device for measuring the weight of the air above us, which is, of course, about fifteen pounds per square inch, or nearly nine tons per square yard, of the earth's surface. Long after its invention it was found that small changes in this weight could be used in weather forecasting. The gasometer, in which gas is collected over water and under a carefully balanced metal cap, was originally a laboratory apparatus for gas measurement, but was later found to be also the ideal means of storing large amounts of gas.

Research, although at first sight so different from invention, consists largely of the design and perfection of apparatus for observation and measurement. A few months ago I met Professor Hertwig, who was the first to observe the actual process of fertilization by the fusion of the nuclei of an egg and a spermatozoon. About a third of modern biology is based on this simple fact, which every educated person to-day takes for granted. My wife asked me whether I thought there were many more discoveries at once as simple and as important to be made in the realm of biology by mere observation. Personally I do think so, but they will depend on the invention of new means of observation as powerful and ingenious as the microscope, which had undergone two hundred years of development when Hertwig made his great discovery.

The usual course of research is to arrive at simple results by complicated means. For example, the very straightforward way in which the genes which control heredity are packed in the nucleus was determined by Morgan and his colleagues, who counted millions of flies of various hereditary compositions. But occasionally the process is much more direct. A distinguished physicist told me that when he started on his scientific career he resigned himself to the prospect that in his lifetime no one would ever see a single atom or measure the diameter of a 'fixed' star. Both of these ends have, however, been achieved; the latter through a rather complicated invention of Michelson's, which does not result in the astronomer seeing or photographing the star's disc. But the atom was seen as the result of a very simple invention by Professor C. T. R. Wilson. When an alpha particle, that is to say, a helium atom without the two electrons which usually form part of it, is shot from a radioactive substance into a gas, it breaks up the gas molecules along its path, and if the gas is super-saturated with water vapour, a trail of mist is formed along the track, which can be seen or photographed. If it hits the nucleus of a gas atom the subsequent track of the nucleus can similarly be seen. In fact, we see the atom in the same sense that we see a shooting star or a rocket at night. Now we can trust a really simple invention like this, and by means of it evidence has been obtained of one of the most sensational results of modern physics, namely, the artificial transmutation of the elements. This was proved to occur when eight out of 400,000 alpha particles, whose tracks were photographed by Blackett, were found to have penetrated the nucleus of a nitrogen atom, knocking a hydrogen atomic nucleus out of it, but remaining imbedded in it themselves.

Biology is waiting for some equally simple method

of seeing the invisible. The microbes responsible for smallpox, some, if not all, forms of cancer, and one of the principal diseases of potatoes and tobacco, to go no further, are all invisible for the simple reason that they are smaller than the wave-length of visible light. In order to photograph them Barnard has invented the ultra-violet microscope, which utilizes invisible 'light' of so short a wave-length as to be deflected by these organisms, if organisms they are. At present this particular invention is too delicate and complicated for ordinary use, but within a generation it ought to be part of the equipment of every biological laboratory, and should render as great services both to biology and medicine as did the improvements in ordinary microscopy which took place during the nineteenth century.

But it will probably be a long time before the ultramicroscope, like the telescope, the galvanometer, the centrifuge (better known as the cream separator), and the thermometer, escapes from the laboratory into everyday life. One of the next laboratory inventions to do so will probably be Kapitza's super-electromagnet, which arose as a solution of the practical problem of creating magnetic fields of ten or more times the intensity of those which can be made with the ordinary magnet. These forces are required to deflect from their paths charged particles moving with enormous speeds. If we could bend the alpha particles fired from radioactive elements out of their paths we could measure their speeds, but it is as futile to try to do this with an ordinary magnet as to deflect a rifle bullet with a bellows. Similarly an ordinary magnet will make the electrons in an atom deviate from their normal tracks just sufficiently to alter the wave-length of its spectral lines by a few hundredths of a per cent. Really to change the spectrum of an element, and thus to arrive at new data as to its cause, one requires a magnetic field about as powerful as that in the atom itself.

If one passed a current large enough to give such a field through a coil for as long as a second, the copper wire would not merely melt, it would boil. Actually a current of about 70,000 amperes, representing 215,000 horse power, is poured for a three-hundredth of a second through a coil as large as one's hand. The source of this power is not a 215,000-H.P. dynamo, but one of ordinary size (13 tons) which is set spinning at a high rate without producing any current, and then suddenly short-circuited through a coil of low resistance. The secret of the design lies largely in the switchgear, which makes and breaks the necessary contacts at immense speed, and must therefore be built from materials of extraordinary strength, besides including features such as a blast of compressed air which blows out the arc which might otherwise be formed when the contact is broken.

It has been calculated by Professor Eddington* that in the centre of the hottest stars there is about twenty times as much energy in a given volume as in the centre of the coil of Kapitza's electromagnet; elsewhere there is enormously less. Any attempt to make electric fields of corresponding intensity would produce sparks as long as small lightning flashes. It is fairly clear that within the next generation these enormous but instantaneous accumulations of energy will be used for some practical purpose, perhaps, for example, to make flashes of light which will reach aeroplanes through a mile of fog.

* If Milne's views are correct, Eddington greatly underestimated the temperature.

Just as laboratory inventions affect the world in general, so a few of the inventions made for purely practical ends exert a profound influence on scientific theory. The steam-engine, though it had been in existence for some time before him, was first made of general utility by Watt, who, though well versed in physics, worked with practical ends in view. It inspired Sadi Carnot to investigate how heat is converted into work. Carnot constructed an imaginary engine which enabled him to give a partial answer to this question. In doing so he enunciated a principle which can be applied to many systems besides heat engines. It has led to a better understanding of chemical reactions, electric batteries, stars, muscles, refrigerators, and the universe, to go no further. But no one was likely to ask the question that Carnot did until a machine had been invented which would convert heat systematically into work.

Another practical invention probably lies at the foundation of geometry. The ancient Egyptian surveyors apparently knew that if they divided a rope into eight equal parts by knots, and made it into a triangle whose sides were in the ratios of three, four, and five, it had a right angle. Pythagoras asked why, and found that it was because the square of five is equal to the sum of the squares of three and four; and any triangle whose sides have this property must be right-angled. In just the same way the steelyard type of balance with a moving weight on an arm was in practical use for some time before Jan Stevin made the theory of it the origin of the new science of statics.

The same thing is happening to-day with wireless communication. Of course it is true that the first wireless set, with a range of a few yards, was made in Hertz' laboratory at Karlsruhe in 1887. But although many men of science co-operated in the development of the modern wireless set, the ends in view were practical. But it has proved a most powerful means of exploration, almost a new sense organ. Everyone knows that radio waves are reflected back by a large layer of any conductor. They travel round the earth and only leak out slowly into space, because they bounce off a conducting layer in the upper atmosphere. By their means we can therefore get information as to the state of affairs at a height far above the range of balloons or aeroplanes, and inaccessible to any of our senses. At present the information so obtained is mainly of theoretical interest. But presumably within a century it will be applied practically in some quite different field, perhaps to weather forecasting or solar physics, since the conducting layer is produced by certain of the sun's rays.

The same apparatus enables us to detect conducting or dielectric layers in the inside of the earth, provided that the soil is dry enough to enable the waves to penetrate the first few feet. It is being used to discover the presence and depth of layers of water, oil, or conducting rocks, which often contain metallic ores. I do not know how far these results have proved valuable to prospectors; they are certainly likely to be of interest to geologists. It will probably be possible to prospect from an airship over dry lands such as Mesopotamia, suspected of containing oil. Just as primitive animals used their senses for strictly limited purposes, and gradually extended their use, employing hearing at first only to detect their enemies or prey, and much later to communicate, so man is using wireless, first as a means of communication, but later to explore the universe.

It is quite likely that when the historians of future ages come to the year 1928 its most striking event will be thought to be, not the Kellogg Peace Pact or the synthesis of cane sugar, but the foundation by Størmer and Hals of the new science of experimental astronomy. Until last year man's attitude to the universe outside his planet had been quite passive. Prayer had been his only attempt to reach out beyond terrestrial limits. The influence of the heavenly bodies could be detected in four ways. Their radiation could be seen, or recorded by photographical or other apparatus. The tidal effects of the moon and sun could be observed. Meteors could be seen, and sometimes picked up and analysed. And magnetic storms and aurorae were found to be due to electrically charged particles and radiation thrown out by the sun. The effects of the sun and moon on living creatures could all be explained by one or another of these influences.

Now when a radio signal of sufficient intensity is sent out, a receiver near the emitting station hears an echo after one-seventh of a second, this being the time taken for the waves to travel round our planet in the narrow layer of air between the surface of the earth and sea and the Heaviside layer. Størmer and Hals found that strong signals sent out from Hilversum in Holland, on the 31·4 metre wave-length, produced echoes, not only after a seventh of a second, but after a time varying between three and fifteen seconds. Even in three seconds, light goes about 560,000 miles, a little farther than to the moon and back. However the moon would not be likely to give a good echo, and in most cases the reflector that sent back the echo must have been beyond the moon. The reflection was most marked during magnetic storms, when the sun is firing electrons and positively charged atoms at the earth, and by an increased output of ultra-violet radiation probably detaching similar particles from the earth's upper atmosphere. Now the earth is a magnet, and charged particles near a magnet move in spirals round its lines of force, and on the whole to-wards its poles. As they hit our atmosphere they make aurorae (northern and southern lights). This is why aurorae are commonest along a circle about 1300 miles from the earth's magnetic poles. As one of these is in Canada, aurorae are seen farther south in North America than in Europe. As they approach the earth the moving particles trace out a surface in interstellar space like the water-drops from a whirling sprayer, and it is from this surface that the signals are reflected, according to Størmer. Another more complicated ex-planation of these phenomena has been suggested, and attempts are now being made to decide which is true.

At the same time, Captain T. L. Eckersley, of the British Broadcasting Company, was investigating those unwelcome noises, atmospherics. During magnetic storms the arrival of a fresh shoal of electrons in the upper atmosphere produces an electromagnetic disturb-ance heard as a click. The click is followed at intervals of about three or four seconds by a series of 'whistlers' becoming gradually fainter and longer drawn out as it is re-echoed from the invisible vault 300,000 miles above us.

We had not learnt earlier of the existence of this gigantic halo surrounding our planet because it happens to be transparent to the sorts of radiation which affect our eye and the photographic plate. Space is, for all we know, full of such invisible objects which we shall gradually discover as we develop new sense-organs like the radio receiving set. The existence of the halo had been deduced mathematically a few years ago, but there must be many more such things which will only be discovered by direct observation.

Incidentally, it is quite characteristic that at the time when Størmer and Hals published their discovery the daily Press ignored it in favour of the antics of a spiritualist who was sending messages to Mars, but did not, like Størmer, receive a reply. On the other hand, a few people are so constituted that discoveries like Størmer's are the principal thing which makes life appear to them to be worth while.

The history of pharmacology shows just the same co-operation of the practical man and the laboratory worker. A study of drugs whose action had been discovered in the past, such as cinchona bark and opium, laid down the principles of pharmacology, and led to the isolation of quinine and morphine. The same principles were then applied to the synthesis or extraction of novel remedies, such as salvarsan and insulin. But medicine benefited still more from the study of another great prehistoric invention, namely, brewing. Pasteur's studies led him from chemistry to the study of alcoholic fermentation, and thence to the investigation of bacteria, which are not very unlike the yeast plant in their behaviour. Yeast makes very little alcohol in the presence of oxygen—otherwise bread would be an intoxicant— and Pasteur's conception that fermentation in life without oxygen led logically to the study of those disease-

P

producing bacteria (for example, that causing lockjaw) which can only develop when oxygen is absent.

In the past the distinction between the scientist and the inventor has been largely economic. The latter has hoped to make money in a more direct way than the former, and often to make it for himself rather than for his fellows. As the centre of gravity in science shifts from physics and chemistry towards biology the chances of individual profit from invention will diminish. But the need for the inventive type of mind will remain. The student who shows no great aptitude for passing examinations often becomes a brilliant doctor or surgeon and receives his due of success, because the medical profession is not governed by men of academic minds. But as scientific principles penetrate such branches of applied biology as agriculture and horticulture, there is very real danger that the practical man who cannot answer a set of written questions on his subject will not get a fair chance of applying his talents. Such men and women are perhaps rare, but they certainly exist. And research is being more and more organized so that a university degree is a better recommendation for a post than natural aptitude. Born researchers are so rare that we dare not neglect any possible source of them. It takes all sorts to make a science.

MY PHILOSOPHY OF LIFE*

I DIFFER in several respects from the other speakers in this discussion. To begin with, I am twenty-seven years younger than the youngest of them. So that I am the only representative of the generation whose finest members died in the Great War. And my intellectual background is very different. As a child I was not brought up in the tenets of any religion, but in a household where science and philosophy took the place of faith. As a boy I had very free access to contemporary thought, so that I do not to-day find Einstein unintelligible, or Freud shocking. As a youth I fought through the war, and learned to appreciate sides of human character with which the ordinary intellectual is not brought into contact. As a man I am a biologist, and see the world from an angle which gives me an unaccustomed perspective, but not, I think, a wholly misleading one.

In describing the world as I see it in so short a time, I cannot avoid being dogmatic. I do not doubt that some of the statements which I am going to make are false. A survey of the beliefs which intelligent men in the past have held as certainties makes that sufficiently clear. One cannot order one's life without a set of beliefs of some kind. But the intellectually honest man must recognize the utterly provisional nature of his beliefs.

* A talk broadcast in November 1929. The other speakers in the same series were G. Lowes Dickinson, Dean Inge, Bernard Shaw, H. G. Wells, and Sir Oliver Lodge.

So when I make an apparently definite statement, I must ask you to put before it some such words as 'It seems to me very probable that . . .' I will now try to state my point of view.

Man lives in two worlds, the visible world which changes with time, and an invisible world whose constituents do not change. But both worlds can only be described as they appear to us, that is, from a human and imperfect standpoint. Among the components of the invisible world are the realities corresponding to mathematical statements like $16 + 9 = 25$. This is a statement of a fact as real as the Albert Memorial, which any sane person must recognize when it is pointed out to him. But unlike the Albert Memorial, it was a reality 10,000 years ago, and will be 10,000 years hence. There are also invisible realities corresponding to scientific laws, and I think also to some of our general notions of what is beautiful and good. These latter realities are harder to apprehend because we approach them through a mist of emotion. We know very little about what may be called the geography of the invisible world. The religions, if I may continue the metaphor, have covered the vacant spaces of its map with imaginary monsters, the philosophies have ruled them with equally imaginary parallels of latitude. But both have affirmed, in opposition to the so-called practical man, that the meaning of the visible world is to be found in the invisible. That has been the secret of their success. They have failed when they tried either to describe the details of the visible world or to dictate the details of conduct in it. The churches are half empty to-day because their creeds are full of obsolete science, and their ethical codes are suited to a social organization far simpler than that of to-day. But they still command the allegiance of a number of intelligent people because, amid a world of transitory interests, they support in some measure the claims of the ideal. I am not a member of any religious body, because I find those claims upheld elsewhere. If I thought that the aims of science and art were merely material I should belong to some church. But I believe that the scientist is trying to express absolute truth and the artist absolute beauty, so that I find in science and art, and in an attempt to lead a good life, all the religion that I want.

I have not very much use for people who are not in touch with the invisible world. At best they are good animals, and too often not even that. The men and women who have done best, both for themselves and their fellows, are those who have brought these two worlds into relation. For example, you can hear me to-night because James Clerk Maxwell fifty-six years ago embodied an extremely important set of properties of electromagnetic waves in a set of equations. Those equations represent an eternal truth—something in the invisible world. Their discovery rendered wireless communication possible. If you do not make any contact with this timeless world (in other words, have no inner life) you have at best a very precarious hold on happiness. Given that contact, you enjoy a very considerable security from the results of misfortune in the visible world, and a complete immunity from boredom. Dean Inge, H. G. Wells, and I agree to a considerable extent about the nature of the invisible world, because we are all, in some degree, disciples of Plato.

One does not come naturally to the realization of eternal truths and values. One is brought there by education in the widest sense. It is one of my principal functions to teach certain scientific truths to students at Cambridge University. Many of them are both able and eager to learn. But others are neither able nor eager. Under our present economic system they are enabled to come to Cambridge because their parents are wealthy. By so doing they keep out others who are better qualified intellectually to learn, and more willing to do so. As a teacher I cannot support a social system which is responsible for this injustice. We have got rid of physical starvation. We still have intellectual, aesthetic, and spiritual starvation, which to my mind are greater evils than any mere economic inequality. Until our educational system is so altered as to give a fair deal to every boy and girl who desires a first-rate education and is capable of benefiting by it, my political views are likely to remain, as they are now, on the left.

There is a worse evil than intellectual starvation, and that is the deliberate suppression of free thought and free speech. I rejoice to live in a country where this evil, though it exists, is less serious than in most other countries. But I believe that even in England freedom of publication is unduly restricted in the names of decency, morality, and so on. There is much more liberty in this respect across the Channel, and no one who has worked beside the French in peace and fought beside them in war can accuse them of degeneracy. So many new ideas are at first strange and horrible though ultimately valuable that a very heavy responsibility rests upon those who would prevent their dissemination.

Moreover, the censorship to which I refer is applied in a very partial way. A book glorifying war may be quite as anti-social, and to my mind quite as obscene, as one glorifying illicit love, but it is never suppressed, and seldom publicly denounced.

I now turn from the world of ideas to the visible world. I am a biologist, that is to say, I study the nature of living creatures, and I naturally look at things from a biological point of view. I feel at home in the world because I know that the other animals, and the plants too, are my blood relations. Even the inert matter has mostly been alive in the past. When I look at a limestone mountain I realize that, grim and lifeless as it appears, it was made by countless billions of my microscopic fellow-creatures. What is more surprising, I think that I can even have some very dim inkling of what it feels like to be limestone. We know material objects in general from the outside. We know our own bodies from the inside. Just as everyone knows what it feels like to be hot, so I know from my own personal experience what it feels like to consist of an abnormally large or small amount of calcium carbonate, of which the limestone mountain is built. In this concrete and detailed way I feel my relationship to the world around me.

I am a part of nature, and, like other natural objects, from a lightning flash to a mountain range, I shall last out my time and then finish. This prospect does not worry me, because some of my work will not die when I do so.

As a biologist I am interested in my body. Most people are only interested in anything below their skins when they are ill. I like to study the performance of mine as my friends do that of their motor-cycles or receiving sets. It amuses me to know what my heart does when I run upstairs, or how quickly my finger-nails grow. To a biologist even a toothache can be interesting. Naturally I regard health as extremely important, far more so than wealth, and I shall regard my life as well spent if I can do a little, by research and education, to make my fellow-creatures healthier. There is still an immense amount to be learnt about health, but if what is at present known to a few were part of the general knowledge, the average expectation of life in this country could probably be increased by about ten years. Two difficulties lie in the way: ignorance and the dissemination of falsehoods. To take a simple example of the latter. Enormous sums are spent in disseminating lies about health in order to advertise medicines and 'health foods' which are generally useless and often dangerous. A widely advertised vitamin preparation contains, besides vitamins, a substance definitely poisonous to children. Under the law of the land I might have to pay thousands of pounds in damages if I mentioned the preparation in question, even if my statement could be proved to be true. On the other hand, I am at liberty to say publicly that diphtheria antitoxin is useless, which is a plain lie.

Now for an example of the prevailing ignorance. When a father advises his son on a choice of occupation, he is generally guided mainly by economic, and partly by ethical considerations. He wants his son to avoid bad wages and bad company. He does not think about bad health, though he may be impressed by the risk of violent death. Yet the health of different occupations differs to an extraordinary extent, and the average man knows very little about the risks of even his own job, let alone his neighbour's. Otherwise no sane man would take up such an occupation as that of metal grinder or barman, with a mortality double that of the average man, when he might become a carpenter or a railwayman, and thus enjoy an expectation of life above the average. Our rulers are equally ignorant of these matters. Protective duties and subsidies are granted quite impartially to healthy occupations like agriculture, and unhealthy ones such as the cutlery trade. When this policy is opposed it is opposed on economic grounds, and never because, by encouraging an unhealthy trade, you are condemning some of your fellow-countrymen to death. All parties agree in putting economic considerations before biological; wealth before health. I could give you plenty more examples of this ignorance if time permitted.

Even a healthy man or woman is incomplete. For a large number of men the main interest in life, the main object of their desires, the main source of their satisfaction, is Woman. For me the fascination of woman is only second to that of science. In most cases man's interest in woman culminates in marriage. Provided it does not then cease, the marriage is generally a success. Successful marriage requires a certain effort by both husband and wife. But, speaking as a happily married man, I can assure you that no other effort is so amply rewarded. Marriage has a biological basis, and would be far more often a success if its biology were generally understood and the knowledge acted on. But you can only study the physiology of marriage against a background of general human physiology. If you do so the facts fit into their proper places. If not, you get a distorted and unhealthy view of them.

The psychological, even the intellectual, benefits of marriage, seem to me to be enormous. If a man has lived for some years in the closest intimacy with a woman, he learns to look at life from her point of view as well as his own. A man who cannot do this is like a man blind in one eye. He does not appreciate the solidity and depth of the world before him. The ideas I am putting before you here are largely my wife's, or at any rate, family ideas, rather than my own private productions. The unmarried woman is perhaps even worse off than the unmarried man; and few women seem to me to be psychologically complete till they have become mothers. During the Middle Ages Europe was far too much influenced by celibate men. To-day much too big a part in public life is played by the celibate woman, and too little by mothers. I find few ideas more genuinely disgusting than that held by many education authorities that a woman ceases to be suitable as a teacher when she becomes a mother. Because I have so high an opinion of marriage at its best, I think that it should be possible to end it if it fails for any of a number of reasons, instead of, as now, for one only. This is called 'undermining the sanctity of marriage'.

Marriage generally brings children. Everyone will agree that it would be an evil if the birth-rate of this country were halved, in which case the population would rapidly fall; or doubled, in which case it would increase too quickly. But they will disagree whether too many or too few children are born at present. I do not know myself, though I am clear that too many children are born in the slums, too few in the well-to-do suburbs. But we shall not arrive at a sensible solution of the population problem till we realize that it is a question of numbers, like the design of a motor-car or the framing of a budget, and cannot be settled by an appeal to abstract principles alone.

COMPARATIVE MORTALITY OF SOME OCCUPATIONS (ENGLAND AND WALES, 1921–1923)

STANDARD MORTALITY FOR CIVILIAN MALES BETWEEN AGES 20 AND 65: (*average* 100)

Anglican Clergymen	56
Insurance Officials	60
Farmers	67
Agricultural Workers	68
Civil Servants (all grades)	80
Railwaymen	83
Electrical Workers	85
Motor Vehicle Drivers	86
Carpenters and Woodworkers	88
Printers	95
Metal Workers	96
Salesmen and Shop Assistants	97
Builders	99
Clerks (not Government)	99
Coal Miners	101
Doctors	102
Textile Workers	105
Makers of Clothing (including Boots)	108
Workers in Amusement Trades	121
Brewers and other Makers of Drinks	126
Glass Workers	128
Horse Drivers	138
Potters	148
Dockers	150
Innkeepers	162
Seamen	177
Bookmakers	193
Barmen	195
Tin and Copper Miners	325
Cutlery Grinders	330

Our present educational system is unjust to children because the majority of them do not get a fair chance, and practically none are taught the truths of science from a human point of view. Science teaching should begin, not with a mythical body in rest or uniform motion, but with the human body. Mine did so begin at the age of three.

Between different men and women there are immense inborn differences which no amount of education can overcome. I do not believe that any training could have made Ramsay MacDonald into Jack Hobbs, or *vice versa*. The ideal society would enable every man and woman to make the best of their inborn possibilities. Hence it must have two characteristics. First, liberty, which would allow people to develop along their individual lines, and not attempt to force all into one mould, however admirable. Second, equality of opportunity, which would mean that, as far as is humanly possible, every man and woman would be able to obtain the position in society for which they were best suited by nature. The waste of human beings under our present system is a far worse evil than any merely economic waste. I believe in democracy because equality of opportunity is impossible where inherited rank or wealth is important, but for no other reason. I do not know what would be the ideal form of government in a community where that equality had been achieved. Democracy appeals to me, not as an end in itself, but as the most hopeful route, at least for England, to a classless society. In a classless society far-reaching eugenic measures could be enforced by the State with little injustice. To-day this would not be possible. We do not know, in most cases, how far social failure and success are due to heredity, and how far to environment. And environment is the easier of the two to improve.

I am a citizen of the British Empire, which includes the great Dominions. My highbrow friends complain that the Dominions have produced little great art or literature. I answer that at least they have done something unique. Before the war the average expectation of life of a baby born in New Zealand was sixty years, in Australia fifty-seven years, in Denmark, the next healthiest country, fifty-six years. England also ran. Since then other countries have caught up to a large extent, but New Zealand and Australia still seem to be leading. I am proud to belong to a Commonwealth which has won the first and second places in the great race against death.

I am also a European, and proud of it. Europe is sick to-day, but it is at least making some attempt to cure that sickness by a federal union of its States. And it still leads the world in science, literature, art, and music. In methods of production the United States are ahead of us, and many Europeans think that we should copy them. Dean Inge believes that the working class in the United States is better off than our own. His opinion is shared in unexpected quarters. When my wife and I were in Moscow last year at a great scientific congress we only saw two propaganda films. One was against alcohol; the other showed the manufacture of Ford cars as an argument for American industrial methods. I take a different view for the following reasons. Though they are still reducing their infantile mortality, since 1921 the death-rate of Americans at every age from thirty upwards has been increasing steadily. Whether as the result of hustle, prohibition, or the spread of medical cults, such as 'Christian Science' and osteopathy, which reject the results of science, America is at present head-ing for death, and not life. Europe has much to learn from America, a little even from Asia, but I do not think that we should imitate either of these continents.

Some of you probably think I have laid too much emphasis on death-rates; I have talked about them for two reasons. Firstly, they are the only means we have of comparing the health of two trades or two nations; and I think that there is a very close connection between health and happiness. Secondly, otherwise well-informed people are ignorant of the facts concerning them.

I am an Englishman, and, what is more remarkable, though of Scottish origin, I believe in England. At the present moment our country counts for less in international politics than during last century. Nevertheless some of our ideas and practices are at present conquering the world. In Moscow, which has rejected the great British invention of Parliament, there was a word which I constantly noticed on posters. It was not 'soviet', nor 'red', nor yet 'revolution', but 'phutbol'. The same is happening all over the world. Spanish bull-fighters are becoming centre-forwards. German students are taking to football instead of slashing one another's faces. And with British sport goes the ethical code called Sportsmanship, which future historians may perhaps consider a British invention as important as Parliament and Railways. I hope to see British sport conquer most of the world. But I am no narrow patriot, and would welcome a French invasion of the British kitchen.

England is only likely to regain her former pre-eminence if we can be ten years ahead of the rest of the world in industry, as we were a century ago. We should, of course, reorganize our industries, but other countries have already done so. We shall not regain our place by doing that. We have probably no great un-developed mineral resources. But we have undeveloped human resources, especially among the children of the skilled artisan class. Our best hope for the future lies in giving them a chance to become Watts and Stephen-sons.

Finally, I am a human being, a citizen of the world which applied science is daily unifying. My own pro-fession of scientific research knows no frontiers and no colour bars. Japanese, Indians, and Chinese, as well as Europeans and Americans, are, or have been, among my colleagues. I am naturally in favour of any measures tending to unify humanity and prevent war. But my views as to the best methods of achieving these aims are not informed by sufficient knowledge to be worth stating. For the same reason I am saying nothing about economics.

I am glad that I live to-day and not at any time in the past. In the 4000 years before about A.D. 1800 civilization had spread over a gradually widening area, but its quality had not greatly improved. A century ago in England children were hanged for theft, and a married woman could own no property. Neither of these evils existed in Ur of the Chaldees 4200 years earlier. In the nineteenth century we doubled our aver-age expectation of life, quadrupled our average real wage, and vastly improved our education and morals. This was made possible, in the main, by the application of science. To-day the whole form of civilization is chang-ing. We are trying unheard-of experiments. The great experiment of Socialism is being tried in Russia and will doubtless be tried elsewhere. We meet with huge and unexpected accidents like the Great War. We shall go on having such accidents so long as our rulers are not merely ignorant of science, but think on pre-scientific lines. (You will remember how the Kaiser talked of the war in terms of 'shining armour', and Mr. Asquith of 'unsheathed swords'.) We have got to learn to think scientifically, not only about inanimate things, but about ourselves and one another. It is possible to do this. A single mind can acquire a fair knowledge of the whole field of science, and find plenty of time to spare for ordinary human affairs. Not many people take the trouble to do so. But without a knowledge of science one cannot understand current events. That is why modern literature and art are mostly so unreal.

We live in a dangerous age, but an extraordinarily interesting one. History is being made on a vaster and quicker scale than ever before. For humanity as a whole I am hopeful. For England I am only moderately hopeful, though I believe that if we are willing to adapt ourselves to the new conditions of life, we may yet be as great a nation as ever. But even if I am blown to pieces in the destruction of London during the next war, or starved to death during the next British revolution, I hope that I shall find time to think as I die, 'I am glad that I lived when and where I did. It was a good show'.

WHAT I THINK ABOUT*

I AM a fortunate man. The majority of my fellows are engaged in work rather as a means of livelihood than for its own sake. I am a biologist and find my job so interesting that I cannot keep my mind off it out of hours. To-day, for example, I have been thinking over three problems. I have been thinking about how ferments work, about the laws of inheritance in dahlias, and about some curious alterations, apparently something like the changing of gear in a motor-car, which take place in my nervous system when I go to sleep. They are all of practical importance, the first and third for medicine, the first for chemical industry, and the second for fruit-growing, because the laws of dahlias and apple trees are probably similar.

But if future antiquaries dig up this document, they will find these questions no more exciting than do most readers of the *Daily Express* to-day. For one of two things will almost certainly have happened. I hope that civilization, and science with it, will have gone on. If so, the excavators will probably be citizens of the World State, and the answers to my problems will be part of general knowledge, as the movements of the planets and the functions of the heart are to-day. But perhaps we shall have slipped back toward barbarism, and the men of Middlesex will gaze across the Thames from the ruins

* A document buried in the foundations of the *Daily Express* new building.

of north London toward a foreign and hostile Surrey. In that case, too, my questions will not interest them. They will probably be treasure hunters, and uninterested in mere paper.

Now that alternative is one of the things of which I think fairly frequently. For it is quite likely that the fate of our civilization will be decided in the present century. I am intensely interested in the Romans and their forerunners, the Egyptians and the men and women of Mesopotamia whose wonderful works are being unearthed while I write. Rome fell, and the lesson is there for us if we could read it. But we cannot. Some attribute its fall to the provision of free bread and amusements to the poor, forgetting that the Empire survived for nearly five centuries after these doles were instituted. Others believe that Rome should have educated her working classes. They forget that she was conquered by still less educated Goths. But even though I cannot rede these riddles I find this large-scale history far more interesting than the details of more recent years.

To-day the old civilization of Europe which we share is adapting itself with some difficulty to the new conditions created by modern industrialism. But it is also threatened by two new types of civilization on its east and west, namely, Communism and Americanism, which claim to be improvements on it. Both of these interest me intensely, and I think that we could copy some features of each with advantage. I should like London to have as good operas as New York and as good biological teaching for the average person as Moscow. But I do not desire that London should adopt either of their standards of personal liberty. I follow with immense interest the fierce and sometimes bloody struggles of the American and Russian Governments against wets and whites respectively, in which they display a vigour and intolerance to be found only in young and growing civilizations. I am particularly interested in the Five-Year Plan of economic expansion in Russia. If it succeeds it will prove that Socialism is a practicable system, and I shall probably live to see some form of Socialism adopted in England. If it fails, Russia may revert to capitalism, and Socialism all over the world experience a great set-back.

I cannot accept the American and Communist ideals because both are too exclusively economic. They agree in taking economic efficiency to be the principal human virtue, even though in one case the benefits go mainly to private individuals, in the other to the State. They are both moving toward the mechanization of life and the standardization of man. Now I am not greatly interested in machinery, and very much so in life. I have not got a motor-car or a wireless set, but I have a large and rather beautiful garden. The people who interest me, and with whom I surround myself so far as I can, are not standardized people, but people who do unexpected things, such as carrying messages from Belgium to Holland during the war, and joining a jazz band or the Communist Party.

And the applications of science that interest me are not those to dead matter, on which our economic system is based, but to life. I am interested not only in medicine, but in the attempt to make ordinary people think about their own bodies in a scientific way. Last year about six thousand women died of cancer of the breast in England and Wales. If they had been treated when the first symptoms appeared, at least four-fifths of them would be alive and healthy to-day. This is only one example out of many. So I think that it is even more important that the general public should learn elementary medicine than the curb-step.

But I find the attempt to apply scientific principles to man in non-medical fields still more enthralling. I am extremely suspicious of most of them. Much of what passes as scientific psychology seems to me profoundly unscientific. The same is true of eugenics, criminology, and many other ologies. The small and cautious army of scientific men and women working in these fields is surrounded by such a horde of vociferous quacks that I can sympathize with the snipers, like Beachcomber, who are fighting a rearguard action against the advance of science. Their verbal missiles generally hit these unwanted allies. But science is advancing. We do know enough psychology to cure some criminals and neurotics, and enough about inheritance to say that some types of feeble-minded should not be allowed to breed. But this does not mean that no criminals should be punished, and no stupid people be permitted to marry. I am interested not only in the progress of science, but in trying to detect the still, small voice of common sense among the shouts of the anti-scientific and pseudo-scientific extremists.

Though not an adherent of any religion, I find religions an absorbing topic. They represent man's attempt to adjust himself intellectually and emotionally to the universe. The intellectual side of this effort interests me mainly because of its fantastic character. The stories of how hundreds of millions of people came to believe in the Immaculate Conception, the uncreated

Koran, or the spiritual advantages of bathing in the Ganges are fascinating both as history and as psychology. But the emotional side seems to me an altogether more serious affair. If science is not to leave a gap which will inevitably be filled by superstition, man must learn to feel himself a citizen of the universe as depicted by science. Fortunately I know that such a state of mind is possible.

I am less interested than the average person in politics because I am convinced that all the political principles of to-day are makeshifts, and will ultimately, though not in my time, be replaced by principles based on science. I am a rather lukewarm supporter of the Labour Party because I consider the present distribution of our wealth unjust, and because in certain industries the age of free competition is passing, and I would sooner see a unified industry controlled by the State than by financiers. I am interested in the movements toward larger economic units, such as the British Empire and the European federation, though I hope that these two movements are not mutually exclusive.

I am only moderately interested in modern literature and art. They are largely experiments with technique, and often unsuccessful. At the moment modern French literature, as represented by men like Giraudoux and MacOrlan, interests me more than English. I am not musical, but even I can notice that broadcasting has improved musical taste.

Women interest me, for I am a normal man, but my interest in them is not mainly intellectual. Children, and especially boys, are another matter. The average boy is something of a scientist, and an artist too. We grownups do our best to knock such nonsense out of him, and generally succeed. But until this process has been successfully carried out, a fairly bright boy is far more intelligent and far better company than the average adult. I am interested in our increasing knowledge of the child's mental processes, but even more in the attempts which are being made, in the face of ferocious opposition, to teach the child the subject which most children find the most fascinating of all, namely, human biology.

By this I do not mean 'sex education', but a knowledge of the child's place in nature, and how his body works. The child represents the hope of humanity. We are not giving our children a fair deal. Many of those who could benefit most from higher education do not get it. Others are given more education than they either want or can assimilate. Hardly any are introduced to the scientific outlook until their minds have been so filled with pre-scientific ideas as to make scientific thought very difficult. I think that justice for children is even more important than justice for adults.

These are some of the topics which occupy my mind. But as a biologist I realize that all men are different, and I do not offer them as a pattern for others.

BIOCHEMISTRY AND MR. GANDHI

AMONG the various demands which Mr. Gandhi is making on the Government of India two are of some biochemical interest. He asks that the Government monopoly in salt should be abolished and that alcoholic beverages should be prohibited. In general a scientific man or woman should be particularly wary of attempting to apply his or her science to the solution of political problems. In politics we make up our minds on very inadequate evidence. So if we do not perform our scientific and political thinking in separate thought-tight compartments, the former is likely to suffer. For this reason I shall not air my views on *Swaraj*, but consider the biochemical part of Mr. Gandhi's programme, since the arguments for and against it would be much the same whatever the system of government.

In England salt is a luxury for most people. We use it as a condiment like pepper, and we could mostly do with a good deal less than we actually consume, as is shown by the fact that we excrete large quantities of it. It does not, of course, follow, as one group of food-faddists believe, that our health would be improved if we ate less salt. But very few of us would suffer in health if a salt-tax resulted in lessened salt consumption. The exceptions in England are interesting, however, because they prove the rule for India.

Some eight years ago Professor Moss, who is at present professor of mining at Birmingham, investigated the dietary of coal miners. At that time wages were relatively high, and the miners could choose their food in a manner which is now impossible. The average miner ate a great deal, for coal-mining is extremely hard work, and work demands food. The food, however, was ordinary food. But in the deeper, and therefore hotter, mines the workers ate astonishing quantities of salty foods such as bacon and red herrings. They apparently also bought a good deal of table salt, and sometimes even relished salted beer. Moss then showed conclusively that this demand for salt was simply to make up the salt lost in sweating.

The world's sweating record, of over two quarts in an hour, is held by an English collier, and as much as eighteen pounds weight may be lost in a single shift in a hot mine. This includes about an ounce of salt, and the average Englishman consumes under half an ounce a day, including that contained in ordinary foodstuffs. A shortage of salt leads to weakness, and to a very distressing form of cramp.

Now in India during the hot weather one sweats for twenty-four hours a day, and to make good the loss over an ounce of salt per day may be needed. Salt is thus an essential component of the diet, and a tax on salt is as undesirable from the biological point of view as would be an excise duty on wheat in England. A physiologist, one may remark, can form no very decisive opinion on the desirability of taxing imported food in England. For if such a tax would tend to lower the vitality of the urban workers it would also probably increase employment in the underpaid but very healthy occupation of agriculture.

But nothing of this kind can be said in favour of the salt-tax in India. It is quite clearly detrimental to the health of the people. No doubt its abolition would dry up an important source of revenue, but in a civilization where biological issues—questions of life and death— were regarded as equally important with economic issues this would not be thought a final objection. The truth is that the salt-tax is a very easy method of raising revenue, which we took over from the East India Company. But the only justification of British imperial rule in India is that it should be—as on the whole it has been—better than that of the Company. The continuance of the salt-tax is a biological argument for *Swaraj*.

Mr. Gandhi also asks for prohibition. Here it might be thought that the biological arguments would be in his favour. For liberty is an ethical and not a biological requisite. A slave may well be healthier than a free man, and enjoy a longer expectation of life. It is possible, though far from certain, that effective prohibition in Britain would make it a healthier country. At first sight it might be thought that this was much more likely to be true in India. Europeans in India generally refrain from alcoholic drinks till sundown, which testifies to a belief that they are more dangerous in a hot than in a temperate climate. Large masses of Indians are on the borderline of starvation, and it might seem that they, at any rate, would be better off if they devoted their meagre incomes to food rather than drink.

So, perhaps, Gandhi argues. But I do not suppose that he or his supporters have heard of the tragedy of Nauru, which was given no publicity whatever in the lay Press, as its only moral is against Government interference with individual liberty. Nauru or Pleasant Island lies in the Pacific Ocean near the equator, and contains large deposits of phosphate. So its inhabitants contribute to the world over-production of food by exporting portions of their native land. They were in the habit of drinking toddy made from fermented palm-juice, and on occasion became very tipsy in consequence, which doubtless lessened their efficiency as excavators. Nauru is governed by Australia under a mandate from the League, and the paternal Government issued an ordinance forbidding the use of toddy. Perhaps the efficiency of the natives as labourers increased, but their infantile mortality rose to 50 per cent. within six months of this law coming into force.

It was found that the children at the breast were dying of beri-beri, a disease due to deficiency of vitamin B1. This substance is nearly absent from the rather monotonous diet of the mothers, but is present in large quantities in the yeast from which the toddy is made. The medical officer of health discovered this fact, and (doubtless after an appropriate delay) toddy was allowed again. The infantile mortality immediately fell to 7 per cent. An account of the Nauru affair was given by Bray in the *Proceedings of the Royal Society of Medicine* for 1930.

The situation in many areas of central India is quite similar. Large sections of the population are on the borderline of vitamin B1 deficiency, and suffer from time to time from mild beri-beri. In these circumstances adults generally survive in rather poor health, but breast-fed children die. This dietary deficiency is at least to some extent supplemented by the use of toddy made from palm-juice, and the efforts of Mr. Gandhi and his followers to prevent the consumption of toddy, by cutting down palm-trees and otherwise, doubtless serve to slow down the increase of the Indian population. So perhaps my objection to them is sentimental. Nevertheless I cannot succeed in repressing my opinion that the infantile mortality of India is already high enough. It is only fair to Gandhi to add that there are no vitamins in distilled liquors, and it is possible that prohibition of whisky might increase the efficiency of the European population of India.

The above facts are mere biology. They will not weigh in a dispute in which both sides ignore biological facts. A compromise will probably be reached by which the salt-tax remains, but toddy is prohibited, thus ensuring the maximum possible interference with liberty and damage to health.

BIRTH CONTROL

THE outstanding moral and political problems of our day are raised by the application of science to human life. The adoption of scientific methods in industry has led to a state of affairs for which many believe that Socialism is the only cure. Scientific war has created a new internationalism. Scientific hygiene has made the population problem actual by diminishing infant mortality.

Until about a century ago most children died young. The British sovereigns from James I. to Anne had thirty-two legitimate children, of whom only ten survived to the age of twenty-one. Conditions were probably worse among the mass of the people. Hence if the numbers of the nation were to be kept up, let alone increased, it was necessary for the average married pair to bring nine or ten children into the world in order that two or three might survive long enough to be parents of the next generation. Under these circumstances, and indeed throughout history until the middle of the nineteenth century, contraception was antisocial, and the Churches were right to condemn it.

To-day it may be desirable that the population of England and Wales should increase slowly. It is certainly undesirable that it should increase during the twentieth century as it did during the nineteenth. If it did so it would reach 118 millions in A.D. 2001. Hence it has become a duty to produce families smaller than were needed when most children died. Assuming that the majority of adults possess normal instincts and therefore marry fairly young, and that wholesale infanticide or abortion is not practised, this end can only be achieved in one of two ways. Either married couples must practise some form of birth control, or they must abstain from cohabitation for years at a time. Both these practices are unnatural, but so is the practice of drinking water from a tap instead of a stream or well, which has so reduced our death-rate that the birth-rate must follow it. The latter alternative, which Canon Lyttelton* calls self-control, may be relatively easy and harmless to some people. There is a good deal of evidence that for others, men and women no worse than their fellows, it is not only difficult (the Anglican marriage service states that it is impossible), but, when practised, physiologically and psychologically harmful. If such couples are to live a healthy married life, and to produce as many parents of the next generation as did their ancestors, but not more, it is their duty to employ contraceptive methods.

But contraception, like other inventions, can be, and has been, appallingly misused. There can be very little excuse save extreme poverty for a healthy couple who voluntarily remain childless, and childless marriages are commoner among the rich than the poor. I am one of those who believe that more birth control is desirable among certain sections of the poor. As long as we have slums we should see that as small a population as possible of the next generation should be born in them. I also believe in contraception for that quite small fraction of the population who transmit inheritable disease or serious abnormality to their children. But I

* In an article to which this was a reply.

am equally clear that too few children are being born in a great many middle-class homes.

The blame for this rests largely on the conspiracy of silence which has enveloped the subject. Those of my women friends who are at the moment doing most for birth control among the poor, and who practise it themselves, are mostly mothers of from six to three children, who have been born at reasonable intervals. These women realize that with contraception, as with other human activities, the guiding principle should be moderation. So long as birth control is regarded as sinful or even shameful, those who practise it will be likely to do so in excess. On the other hand, many women will be prematurely worn out by too frequently repeated pregnancies which they could easily have spaced out.

So far as can be ascertained from the figures before me, to prevent a decrease of the population a married woman should have, on the average, about $2\frac{1}{2}$ children. Allowing for natural sterility and early deaths, the average healthy mother should have just over 3. Even if the emigration rate were to increase to pre-war figures, an average of 4 would lead to an increase in the population which would ultimately cause gross overcrowding. Any couple with less than two, or more than four, children may therefore ask themselves whether they are doing their duty to humanity. Only exceptionally healthy and intelligent parents should aim at a higher figure than five. I think that the question of the morality of family limitation can be answered along such lines as these. One can no more answer it exactly than state the exact sum which a family ought to spend on charity or amusements. One can only point to examples of excess and defect.

In the short space remaining I will briefly answer some of Canon Lyttelton's other questions. In the past, most great men were members of large families, because most families had to be large if the race was to survive. Thus Gibbon was the only survivor of seven. The first child is slightly handicapped by a special danger of injury at birth, the latter children of large families by maternal exhaustion. The second to the fifth have probably the best chances in life.

The super-tax was introduced by Mr. Lloyd George to confer 'the benefits of impecuniosity'* where those benefits can be best conferred. I am of opinion that still more of these benefits might be lavished by the State on those super-tax payers who have few or no children. Character, in my experience, can be adequately trained in small families. But the correct methods are naturally different from those suitable for large households. In particular the parents of an only child should give it the companionship which its brothers and sisters would otherwise have provided.

Experts may agree that if populations continued to increase at their present rate the world will be over-crowded in a few centuries. As, however, rates of increase are changing much more rapidly than the populations themselves, this conclusion has a merely academic interest. From the point of view of world peace it is, however, obviously desirable that certain nations which have not yet reached a very high grade of civilization should begin to limit their rate of increase.

One reason why there is so much hesitation in practising the sterilization of the unfit is that, except in

* Here I am referring to the article by Canon Lyttelton, to which this was a reply.

the case of imbeciles, birth control is an alternative which appears to many far more humane. Another reason is that such sterilization has, at least in one country, been used as an instrument of class war. But the greatest reason is the difficulty of deciding who is unfit. There is an ancient saying which both those who condemn contraception and would-be sterilizers* of their fellow-creatures might well bear in mind: 'Judge not, lest ye be judged'.

* This objection does not of course apply to strictly voluntary sterilization.

THE STORY OF MY HEALTH

M Y story has no moral. Three of my grandparents lived to be over eighty, one to be
a hundred. My parents are both alive. So if I
enjoy good health, this is probably not through my
having observed any laws, but because, from the point
of view of mere living at least, I am well born. Also up to
the age of twelve I was well looked after. In my cradle I am
told that I screamed so loud as to rupture myself on both
sides, and I owe my continued existence to my mother's
nursing. My diet was a compromise. My milk was
always boiled, for in those days milk-borne tuberculosis
was a greater danger to children than it is to-day. But
apart from unboiled milk and ice-cream off barrows I
was allowed to eat and drink what I chose.

We did not know about vitamins in those days, but
it was known that a monotonous diet brought on certain diseases, whose investigation later led to the discovery of some of the vitamins. Besides Marie Lloyd
had just enunciated the important physiological principle that

A little of wot yer fancy does yer good.

My father was a physiologist, and I was brought up
on this principle, particularly as regards jam. I ate a
great deal of unripe fruit and other foods which were
generally supposed to be harmful. But the only things
that have ever made me seriously ill are temperance
drinks, especially raspberry vinegar and coca-kola. For-

tunately at the age of eleven, when on a cycling expedition, I discovered cider. In those days children could go into pubs, and thereafter I stuck to water, milk, or honest alcoholic beverages, except when staying with relatives who occasionally poisoned me with temperance drinks.

I ought to have died when I was nine, as I broke my skull in a cycle accident. The surgeon's prognosis was that I would probably die, very probably be mentally deranged, and certainly be deaf in one ear. As I can hear rather well, I have promised my skull to my friend Sir Arthur Keith should I predecease him. He wants to know how the works of my internal ear were mended. So if ever I am mysteriously murdered, Scotland Yard will know of a possible motive for the deed.

At the age of twelve I went to Eton with a scholarship. The diet was monotonous and the cooking shocking. The matron was more interested in our souls (from an Anglo-Catholic angle) than our bodies. Probably for this reason I had my first serious illness, an inflammation of the middle ear which had not been smashed in my accident. After this I had somewhat more money to spend on food, and was able to supplement my diet as I wished. During my last three years I escaped, during two of the three terms, from compulsory games, and found that I did very well with less exercise than most of my fellows. This incidentally enabled me to do some work. At Oxford I rowed occasionally, but discovered that after several months without any exercise, not only was I very well, but I was perfectly able to row in a race untrained, and help to win it.

During the war, apart from a couple of wounds, I was 'in the pink' until 1918. Then, at a bombing school in Central India, I had two strokes of bad luck. I had got on very well for a year without a mosquito net. But my servant, Muhammad Akbar Khan (which means approximately Lord Glorified Larger), wishing for the 10 per cent. commission which all Indian servants scrounge out of their masters' purchases, persuaded me to buy one. Now sandflies can get through the holes in mosquito nets, and my net evidently put them on their mettle. Within a week I was down with a particularly nasty fever transmitted by these insects. Up till then I had lived on the excellent and nearly vegetarian diet which Indians have found suitable for their climate. Indeed, as I had been inoculated against typhoid, I drank unboiled water, chewed betel nut bought at road-side booths, and generally behaved in an un-English manner. But now the mess-president switched me over to a meat diet, and I developed the most beautiful jaundice, which possibly saved my life, as I was not sent back to the trenches.

When I was demobilized I had to face a serious situation. I had developed the exercise habit during the war. I knew that exercise was not essential to my health, and that it took time which might have been devoted to work or to enjoying life. But to forgo one's daily exercise is almost as hard as to give up one's daily injection of cocaine or morphine. For six miserable months I struggled with the craving till I had mastered it. Now I know that I can keep fit on nothing more than a daily cycle ride to and from my work for eleven months, and then go off for three weeks of mountaineering without any danger of falling back into my former vice when I return.

But I did not at first cut down my diet to suit my

sedentary habits. Perhaps that was why I developed appendicitis, which is a disease mainly afflicting the overfed classes of society. As my appendix continued to trouble me, arrangements were made for my formal opening, and it was removed before an admiring audience of my pupils, who, being students of medicine, were privileged not merely to attend the operation, but to cut the peccant organ into sections for microscopic examination. Otherwise, save for a complaint which delicacy forbids me to mention, but which I put down to the effects of India, my health has been excellent.

But I have cut down my food. I breakfast on porridge and milk, drink coffee in the middle of the day, take four slices of bread and jam with my tea, and have my real meal at 8 P.M. My cook, although a Belgian, can make real Scottish porridge, besides many other good things, and I probably owe much of my good health to her ability.

I find that I have forgotten to mention colds. I was brought up to sleep with the window open, and had about a cold a month through the winter. Since I married, my bedroom window is shut in cold weather, and I only get about two colds a year. Of course when a number of people sleep in one room, the windows must be kept open. If this is not done, anyone suffering from a great variety of diseases, including diphtheria and cerebro-spinal meningitis, will give it to the others. But except in over-crowded sleeping quarters or in hot weather, I do not believe in open windows at night.

This is the story of my health. But I do not for one moment suggest that what suits me would suit everyone else. Many people appear to become genuinely ill without exercise. For all I know, my nightly whisky and soda would poison Lady Astor or Mr. Foot. I do not prescribe for them; nor do I see why they should prescribe for me. I have experimented on myself, and at times taken more food, beer, and other good things, smoked more tobacco, and done more work than was good for me. I know the symptoms of excess in each case, and I can stop before they come on. My advice to others is to take the obvious steps, such as vaccination, to avoid infections, but apart from that, to study oneself in a scientific spirit, find out a way of life which suits one, and live according to it. The perspicacious reader will also have deduced that I do not take occasional lapses from health very seriously. Nor should he or she.

ILLNESSES THAT MAKE US HEALTHIER

SICKNESS, madness, and premature death seem at first sight to be examples of waste of human material. Here are a good worker who has been crippled in the prime of life, a devoted mother who has died leaving orphaned children, a sensitive artist who has lost his reason. For the individuals most nearly concerned these are unmitigated tragedies. But from the point of view of the community there is always a redeeming feature if they are studied scientifically. Not only can an examination of such misfortunes save others from their like, but it may even help normal people to a better life.

For we scientists are not supermen. Far from it. We are somewhat more intelligent than the average, and a great deal more critical of our theories. But our minds work in the same way as other men's minds. The greatest living experimental physicist once said to me, 'If we could see an inch in front of our noses we should discover the whole of physics in one generation'. The man who said that can see, so to speak, a fraction of a millimetre in front of his own nose. Some of his experiments which to others appeared as shots in the dark were successful and revealed new principles. But most scientific theories are based on analogy with known facts, and careful experiments must be devised to see if they are correct, which they generally are not. We can only go step by step, and commonly only arrive at a general law by studying its most striking cases first.

The history of medicine is full of examples. It had long been known that some diseases were contagious. But it remained for Pasteur to show that the contagion was something alive, first with a disease of silkworms, and then with anthrax, which at that time commonly attacked sheep, and occasionally men. Later on Koch and others showed that a number of diseases such as cholera were carried by water, and a proper organization of the water supply has abolished them in civilized countries, whilst elsewhere drinking water must be boiled or sterilized. Only very gradually, as the result of such successes, did the medical profession and the general public come to believe in the theory that most diseases are caused by living germs. In consequence, a search was made for the agents of diseases which were not obviously infectious.

Another great step forward was made when it was found that malaria is caused by a living creature which makes its home in our blood corpuscles and is transferred from one man to another by mosquitoes. It took some time to prove this, as against the older theory that it was due (as its name suggests) to the bad air of the swampy regions where the mosquitoes flourish. Fortunately the malaria parasite is easily visible with a microscope, so its life-history could be worked out in detail. But for the conclusive proof in the case of malaria it is doubtful if anyone would have undertaken the research necessary to prove that typhus fever is carried by another insect, the louse. For that research was both laborious and dangerous. A number of the men who showed how typhus is spread died of it in the process. Our ancestors, who knew typhus as gaol-fever, thought that the contagion was carried by the air, and judges occasionally put rue and other aromatic herbs in their nostrils in a vain attempt to protect themselves, instead of seeing that the prisoners had baths and clean clothes. Even now the proof that typhus is carried by lice is less conclusive than the proof that malaria is carried by mosquitoes, because the typhus parasite is too small to be seen at all clearly even with the best microscopes. But the circumstantial evidence is strong enough. Delousing abolishes typhus.

So in order to stamp out typhus it was necessary that some men should die of cholera, others of malaria. The microbe of typhus is only one of a group which are ultra-microscopic. Another equally small or smaller organism causes the common cold. When colds are as rare as typhus, fifty or a hundred years hence, it will be because the study of such diseases as typhus had shown how to tackle an invisible enemy.

Another group of diseases is due to food which does not contain enough of one or another of the vitamins. The first diseases which were conclusively shown to be of this kind were scurvy and beri-beri. The former was common among sailors who were restricted to such food as ship's biscuits and salt meat on long voyages. The latter is mainly found in rice-eating countries such as Java and Japan. Only later did Sir Thomas Barlow discover that many babies in England suffer from a mild form of scurvy, easily preventable by a few spoonfuls of orange juice a day. The sailors who died of scurvy called attention to the problem and saved the babies born a hundred years later from a good deal of suffering and a certain number of deaths. Later rickets fell into line, although many doctors had ascribed it to lack of sunshine or bad heredity. They were probably right in both cases; however, no baby will get rickets, no matter how bad its heredity or how dark its home, provided it is given enough vitamin D to eat. But a study of the effects of a shortage of vitamin D on puppies, made by Professor and Mrs. Mellanby of Sheffield, proved that the rickety animals always had bad teeth, and a dose of the vitamin sufficient to prevent rickets was not always enough to make the teeth normal. Rickets are only a severe symptom of a shortage of vitamin D. Bad teeth are often due to a slight shortage, though of course that is not their only cause. Nothing is more likely to cause unemployment among dentists thirty years hence than a good supply of vitamin D for expectant and nursing mothers, and growing children, to-day. You can buy it at the chemist's; but if you are an adult, and eat an orange every other day, and liver once a week, you will probably get enough vitamins for most purposes, including some which you cannot yet buy from the chemist.

If you are dying, perhaps slowly and painfully, of a disease, you can, if you are an altruistic (I prefer the English word good) person, extract a quite considerable amount of satisfaction from the thought that your sufferings will save someone else from a similar fate. This is often the case, provided the patient is adequately studied both before and after death, and it is especially so in the case of rare diseases. For example, tumours of the brain are fortunately not very common, but if not cut out they are generally fatal, first causing paralysis, blindness, convulsions, or mental derangement, and finally killing the patient, often after a period of great suffering. Now the surgeon cannot hunt about in a living brain for tumours. He must know just where to operate if he is to have any chance of saving the patient. The necessary knowledge is gradually being gained by comparing the symptoms during life with the findings after death. Only after the comparison has been made on a number of patients dare the surgeon take the risk of operating. So everyone who dies of a brain tumour is saving the life of a fellow-creature *provided his or her brain is examined after death*. And everyone who refuses such an examination of their next-of-kin is condemning another man or woman to death. The same is true in less degree of many other diseases. The objection to a post-mortem examination seems to me a piece of utterly unjustifiable sentimentalism. It would be irrational in a complete materialist, and is still more so if one believes that the soul leaves the body at death.

Personally I go much further, and propose to be dissected for the purpose of anatomical teaching when I am dead. So, incidentally, do my mother and my wife. The more dissections a medical student can perform, the more skilled will he or she be when they come to operate on a living patient. The doctrine that death for others is a noble thing is the very core of Christianity. I may not have the luck to die in saving someone else, but I certainly do not intend to deprive myself of the satisfaction of thinking, as I die, that my death will be of some use. Besides, I can refuse to attend other people's funerals without breaking the golden rule, because I certainly do not want anyone to attend my own, which I hope will be a voyage in a van to the nearest anatomical laboratory.

Just the same is true of mental disease. Science has to begin with the most glaring cases. One type of insanity can be definitely relieved by giving the patients malaria or some other fever, which is cured after it has cooked the germs concerned. Others, though they cannot yet be cured themselves, have been of immense value to some people. Janet and Charcot in France attributed the behaviour of certain lunatics to the workings of the subconscious mind, which is irrational, but yet obeys laws of its own. Freud followed up this work on patients who were on the borderline of madness, and showed that even in sane people a great deal of unreasonable behaviour can be traced down to the unconscious. We all have little patches of madness, mental cupboards containing skeletons of which we are secretly ashamed, and whose existence we hide from our conscious thought. Freud's principle is to let in light and air into these cupboards, which is only possible if we cease to be ashamed of the skeletons.

For example, I should derive considerable satisfaction from bashing in other people's faces with a spanner. When I got the opportunity of killing other people during the war I enjoyed it very much, though it is now more fashionable to say that one hated every moment of it. If I were ashamed of that particular skeleton (which is really a quite respectable relic of primitive man) I should hide my real motives from myself, invent excellent moral reasons for violence, and go forth in holy anger and pious grief to smite the wicked, or at least encourage others to do so. As it is, I view that kind of moral indignation in myself and others with profound suspicion, and try to work off my steam in other ways. But if Freud had not encouraged me to look a little below the surface of my mind I might be preaching national war or class war. Revolution and war are forms of collective lunacy. They may sometimes be the lesser of two evils, as madness may be the alternative to suicide. But their psychological roots lie deep in our natures, and they will only be abolished from within. In other words, we shall not understand the mad nation until we know more about the mad man, and homicidal maniacs may yet play an indirect but important part in ending war.

A MATHEMATICIAN LOOKS AT SCIENCE

IN this age of applied science it is gradually being realized in some circles that, if civilization is to continue, scientific thought must be applied to men as well as to nature. Hence the public is beginning to try to understand how scientific workers approach a problem. And here they are at once confronted with the curious but, as we shall see, quite intelligible inarticulateness of most scientific workers. In England the most widely read writers on science are Russell, Eddington, and Jeans. It is not a mere coincidence that all three are first-rate mathematicians, that is to say experts in the use of symbols. Russell and Jeans, so far as I know, have never published the result of a single observation of nature, much less of an experiment. Eddington is a great observer, but not a great experimenter. Hence although the three differ on fundamental problems, from the existence of God downwards, their scientific experience is almost wholly confined to the art of organizing known facts, rather than of eliciting new facts from nature. Hence their account of the scientific outlook is inevitably different from that of the laboratory worker.

This difference appears as early as the introduction to Russell's book.* While he realizes that science is both knowledge and technique, he states that the technique, though practically important, has little intrinsic value.

* *The Scientific Outlook.*

253

Now as a physiologist I note that I need as large an area of brain to control my hands as my vocal organs. And as a scientific worker I note that some of my colleagues appear to do most of their thinking with their hands, and are extremely inexpert at the use of words. One Fellow of the Royal Society, I am told, did not even learn to talk till he was ten years old. He is still a rather inexpert talker, but he designs and makes apparatus that can solve problems which have appeared insoluble to better talkers and mathematicians.

So I suspect that Russell, in spite of an attitude far more sympathetic to science than that of most mathematicians, let alone philosophers, has only grasped so much of the scientific outlook as is expressed in words or symbols rather than actions. This appears in his first chapter, where he describes, as examples of scientific method, the work of Galileo, Newton, Darwin, and Pavlov. We are told that Galileo made a telescope. But we get no indication of the fact that this was an immense technical achievement. One cannot read Galileo's dialogues without feeling that he thought like an engineer rather than a mathematician.

In the case of Newton there is no hint that besides inventing the calculus and the law of gravitation, he actually experimented on optics, which he advanced as much as anyone before or since.

So with Darwin. We read that he travelled, observed, and reflected, but not that his experiments on plant-breeding, besides being highly ingenious, were extremely accurate.

It is fairly clear that Russell regards the skilful manipulation of symbols as an activity altogether more respectable than that of material objects, though he never states this belief explicitly. This eminently academic view permeates his whole thought. Galileo's arguments purporting to prove that the earth's movement was conformable to Holy Writ were probably no better than those of the inquisitors who held the contrary view, but his telescope was better than their eyes.

Russell's knowledge of biology is also not on a level with his knowledge of physics. Indeed he makes a few demonstrably false statements about biology. And it is going too far to say, as he does, that biologists regard natural selection as inadequate to account for evolution. Some biologists hold this view. Others (including myself) are rather more Darwinian than Darwin. Nor (I hope) is it true that mathematics are inapplicable to the problem of evolution, as I happen to have published a mathematical theory of natural selection in nine instalments, and there are more to come. For the same reason he says very little about statistical methods, which have been developed, largely by biologists, to enable us to deal with cases where we cannot get information as complete as the physicist can sometimes obtain, and which offer one of the few hopes of introducing scientific method into politics.

I feel that Russell's preoccupation with mathematical physics is largely responsible for the pessimism which he attributes to scientists. 'While science as the pursuit of power becomes increasingly triumphant,' he writes, 'science as the pursuit of truth is being killed by a scepticism which the skill of the men of science has generated'. As a director of research in two laboratories I find no signs of this scepticism among the workers there, nor do I find it among my colleagues who are researching in experimental physics. They mostly hold that if Eddington or Russell really believe that the universe is expanding, or has no coherence or order, this merely shows that symbols can be as intoxicating to mathematicians as are ordinary words to politicians.

In spite of these limitations in his outlook, Russell is much more sympathetic with the scientific outlook than most other popular writers on similar topics; and just for this reason, the last, and in many ways the most interesting, part of his book, which deals with the scientific society, appears plausible to a scientific worker. Russell foresees the application of scientific technique to social problems, and the result is not an ideal society, even if it be somewhat more desirable than our own. He believes that, after another European war, the United States will probably take over the organization of the ruins; and that the resulting world-government by millionaires will probably be replaced by a government of experts. It would be interesting to know how far the current economic collapse in the United States and the apparent success of the Russian five-year plan would induce him to modify this view were he writing to-day. In any case Communism is rapidly becoming a matter of government by technicians, which accounts for its success.

In the scientific State there will be no war or real poverty, and a minimum of disease. The working class will be educated to be docile, industrious, punctual, thoughtless, and contented. They will probably largely be sterilized, so as to allow them unlimited frivolous love affairs. The ruling class will continually provide them with new amusements, and devise new methods of propaganda to increase their reverence for their governors.

These latter, selected by psychological tests in early childhood, and specially treated to secure the maximum of ability, will be trained in intelligence, self-command, and leadership. But they will combine these with a fanatical loyalty to their class and its ideals, and a contempt for other human values. Individual love will be regarded as anti-social, and likely to lead to complexes. Science will gradually become more technical and more cruel, and the social order will slowly develop instability as other tyrannies have done in the past. The detail of such a social system, and the fate of an unscientific intellectual in it, are described in a novel called *Man's World* written by my wife in 1926 (and also in Huxley's *Brave New World* of 1932). Russell agrees with her forecast in most respects.

Such a prophecy is natural enough in view of the author's bias already noted. 'It is only in so far as we renounce the world as its lovers that we can conquer it as its technicians', he writes. 'But this division in the soul is fatal to what is best in man.' My own experience as a biologist is exactly to the contrary. Until I took to scientific plant-breeding I did not appreciate the beauty of flowers. If I find out how to produce a certain change in the composition of my blood I want to know what it feels like, to appreciate it as a fact of life as well as a fact of chemistry. Thus I regard it as interesting that, after taking the largest quantity of calcium chloride on record, I dreamt that Edward Lear had written and illustrated a life of Christ. It was a strange book, but not essentially irreverent. Unfortunately, the only detail of it which remains clearly in my memory is Pontius Pilate's moustache.

As science permeates psychology I look for such a

heightening of human self - consciousness as would wreck the complacency of Russell's ruling class. His scientific State is a State of engineers rather than of biologists. It is perfectly possible that his forecast is correct. But if so, it will be because biology developed too late to take its rightful place beside physics.

Like all Russell's books, including *Principia Mathematica*, this is exceedingly witty. Wit consists in the unexpected but appropriate juxtaposition of ideas, and it was just the capacity for such a juxtaposition which made him a great mathematician. Thus we read of physicists: 'Only mathematics and mathematical logic can say as little as the physicist means to say', and of psycho-analysts: 'I suppose that for practical purposes "phantasy" is what the patient believes, and "reality" what the analyst believes'. But perhaps the wittiest thing in the book is the examinations of the theological deductions of Eddington and Jeans. Eddington regards it as probable that physical laws do not hold for certain atomic events, and thinks that mind may act on the physical world by taking advantage of this fact. Jeans, on the other hand, is so impressed by the reign of precise mathematical laws in the universe that he postulates a mathematical creator. It would thus seem that in so far as Eddington is right, Jeans's creator has scamped his work. But in so far as the universe attains a mathematical perfection worthy of that hypothetical being, it leaves no place for free will, and the apparent influence of our minds on it is an illusion. Russell contrives to knock the heads of his distinguished colleagues together with a resounding crack, but I do not feel that he is justified in writing that the bulk of eminent physicists have made pronouncements that materialism is disproved and religion re-established. I do not recall any such statements by Barkla, Bragg, Richardson, Rutherford, or Thompson, to mention five British Nobel prizemen in physics. The bulk of eminent physicists confine their attention to physics and do not enter into theological controversy on either side.

This book will be widely read, and deserves to be. But its readers will do well to remember that its author is an intensely individual human being, endowed with rather strong emotions which inevitably influence his thought except when he is thinking according to certain definite rules. Now there is a technique for thinking scientifically about matter, but as yet none for thinking scientifically about science, except perhaps in the writings of the Russian authors who are investigating the influence of economic conditions on scientific output. Every scientific worker will be interested to learn what is Russell's outlook on science, and will benefit by seeing himself as another sees him, when that other has the originality and intellectual courage of a Russell. But even Russell is not a passionless thinking-machine: the subject matter of the book is science, but the outlook is Russell's.

THE NEW DEISM

SIR JAMES JEANS is already well known to the
intelligent public as the author of that excellent
summary of modern astronomy *The Universe
Around Us*. In *The Mysterious Universe* he covers some
of the same ground, but is mainly occupied with the
basal hypotheses of modern physics, and, in the last
chapter, with theology. It is quite true, though one did
not gather it from certain summaries in the daily Press,
that the author concludes his final and theological
chapter with the statement that 'everything that has
been said, and every conclusion that has been ten-
tatively put forward, is quite frankly speculative and
uncertain'. Few rationalists would object to the teaching of religion in elementary schools were this phrase
repeated sufficiently often. But in practice we shall be
told from many pulpits that the book in question recon-
ciles science and religion, regardless of the fact that
no religion has ever regarded its views as speculative
or uncertain. For this reason it is worth pointing
out why, in the opinion of the reviewer, some of Sir
James's conclusions are somewhat less plausible than
he supposes.

His work in the past has been mainly on gases and
on the rotation of stars. In consequence, his account
of atomic physics is mainly second-hand, though none
the less readable for that. And in his own field he is
occasionally unduly dogmatic. Thus the criticisms of
his own theories as to the origin of the planets by

Jeffreys and as to the central temperature of the stars by Milne are completely ignored; and so is the evidence of Shapley and Payne that certain stars, unlike the sun at the present time, are surrounded by so much meteoric matter that they are not necessarily losing weight by radiation. Sir James may be right on all these points, but on none of them do his views command anything like unanimous support.

Apart from the last chapter, there are two points which will be of most interest to the philosophically minded, namely, the account of wave mechanics and Heisenberg's principle of indeterminacy, and the evidence that the universe is running down. There seems to be little doubt of the fact that we cannot simultaneously determine the position and speed of a moving particle with complete accuracy; and what is more, that we cannot approach accuracy indefinitely by expending more effort. As Sir James Jeans states the case, this inaccuracy is part of nature, and is bound up with the attempt to describe phenomena in terms of particles rather than waves. But other physicists do not place the antinomy in the external world at all. To quote a recent paper by Prof. C. G. Darwin on wave mechanics: 'If these ideas are admissible, we can put the inexplicable feature of the quantum theory, the irreconcilability between wave and particle, in exactly the place where we have got in any case to have an inexplicability, in the transfer from objective to subjective'. In other words, it is not nature, but our perception, which is indeterminate. Again, Professor Darwin may be wrong, as his grandfather Charles Darwin occasionally was, and if he is right the 'real' world is very queer indeed. But on his view it is not indeterminate, and it is doubtful whether Sir James is entirely justified in neglecting his work.

The origin of wave mechanics, which are inevitably paradoxical, but not perhaps quite as paradoxical as we are led by our author to believe, is very interesting. Electrons and protons, when studied in rapid motion, and not as components of atomic or molecular systems, seemed to be very simple in their physical properties. But together they form systems whose properties are highly complicated. For example, a hydrogen atom, made from one of each, can radiate a spectrum more complex than a piano scale. Now when such phenomena occur in the field of biology, there is a strong tendency to speak of the 'emergence' of a new type of whole, with qualities unpredictable from those of its parts. This problem held up theoretical physics for a whole generation. But the physicists refused to surrender to holism. Finally de Broglie solved it by ascribing undulatory properties to the electron and proton even when they did not form part of an atomic system. These properties have been experimentally verified with striking success. The moral is one of enormous hope for thorough-going monism. Most biologists are working towards an explanation of living organisms in terms of their constituents. In order to do this we shall doubtless have to postulate unexpected properties in those constituents. But as long as the human race can produce experimenters of the calibre of Davisson, Germer, and Thompson, we are likely to find them. Wave mechanics thus represents the most serious inroad yet made on the doctrine of emergence, which attempts to set up barriers to the progress of scientific interpretation.

On page 144 Sir James Jeans repeats the view that

the entropy of the universe 'must have had a beginning; there must have been what we may describe as a "creation" at a time, not infinitely remote'. Let us examine this statement. If we write an equation for entropy in terms of time, then for a certain negative (*i.e.* past) value of the time the entropy becomes zero. Now nothing is commoner in physics than to find an equation which fits a set of facts extremely well over a limited range, but then leads to an absurd result. For example, the equation for the density of the air in terms of its height leads to the conclusion that this density suddenly becomes zero at a finite height. Actually the equation works very well for the first five to eight miles, and then ceases to work. A similar situation is not perhaps impossible as concerns entropy. At least two physical alternatives are open. One is the possibility, discussed by Poincaré and others, and persistently ignored by Sir James Jeans, that the universe is a 'fluctuation', *i.e.* that it has run down in the past and built itself up again by random processes. Another is suggested by a recent paper of Mosharaffa on the duality of matter and radiation. According to Mosharaffa's views it seems plausible that a universe where the matter had mainly dissolved into chaotic radiation would proceed once more towards aggregation, as did the world of chaotic gas which Sir James believes was the initial state of our present universe.

But if such alternatives are ultimately shown to be impossible, why 'creation'? We work back, by means of mathematical physics, to a time when our equations must in some way be modified, and we are then to desert reasoning for the conjectures of certain ancient Semitic races, whose cosmogony, where it can be tested, is more often wrong than right. It is difficult to put down Sir James's liking for the creation hypothesis to anything but the historical accident that that particular myth has been incorporated in our prevailing religion.

And now for theology. Our author is impressed by the fact that by far the most adequate account of the physical universe which we can give is a highly abstract mathematical account, and hence regards it as probable that the universe consists of thoughts in the mind of a pure mathematician. I am myself rather sympathetic to an idealistic interpretation of the universe, but I must admit that all Sir James's arguments can very easily be turned round in favour of materialism. 'It can hardly be disputed', he says, 'that nature and our conscious mathematical minds work according to the same laws.' And again, 'to my mind, the laws which nature obeys are less suggestive of those which a machine obeys in its motion than of those which a musician obeys in writing a fugue, or a poet in composing a sonnet'. Now, supposing our mental activities to be a particular aspect of atomic behaviour, what should we expect? Clearly, in so far as they are utilitarian, they will conform to patterns impressed on them by biological needs through the agency of natural selection. We shall think in certain ways because it has paid our ancestors to do so. But in so far as our thought is spontaneous and not directed to some end of biological value, we shall expect it to mirror the inner nature of atoms. This seems to me just as legitimate an argument as the author's, and if so he has only added one more item to the strange list of analogies between mind and matter, analogies which perhaps neither the idealistic nor the materialistic metaphor can fully explain. To the biologist any views con-

cerning mind which make no reference whatever to
brain appear to neglect half the available evidence.

But even if we follow our author to the end of his
argument, the result is profoundly unsatisfying (though,
of course, none the less probable for that). 'We discover that the universe shows evidence of a designing
and controlling power that has something in common
with our own individual minds—not so far as we have
discovered, emotion, morality, or aesthetic appreciation,
but the tendency to think in a way which, for want of
a better word, we describe as mathematical.' That is
clearly the statement of an intellectually honest man,
but the power in question is not likely to become the object of a cult, or even, like the god of deism, the basis of
a morality. There are, I think, other possible mytho-
logies at least equally compatible with what we know
of the universe, and far more satisfying to those human
emotions which find their outlet in religion. One such
is developed in Mr. Stapledon's very remarkable novel
Last Men and First Men, which envisages the future
evolution of group minds with as definite a physical
basis as our own (which from the cellular point of
view are group minds) and leaves open the possibility
of such a mind embracing the whole universe.

I think one can explain Sir James Jeans's mythological
preferences as follows. In scientific work we are always
framing hypotheses. But we do not trouble to develop
those which cannot be tested by experiment or observation. Thus the apparently extravagant hypothesis that
the universe is finite and expanding leads to certain
predictions about the colour of light from spiral nebulae
which can be tested. But the mathematician builds, so
to speak, in the void. This is perfectly legitimate pro-

vided he does not suppose that the real world must conform to his theories. It may or may not do so. The creation hypothesis can only be tested by its observable consequences to-day. One would suppose that an intelligent creator would intervene, by further creative acts, in favour of the finite minds of his creation. Sir James Jeans admits that there is no evidence for this view. Until such evidence is forthcoming I shall continue to regard creation as an unverified hypothesis. But as an introduction to the more speculative side of modern physics I can strongly recommend *The Mysterious Universe*.

IF JESUS LIVED TO-DAY

MOST of my readers are, at least nominally, Christians. I am not. I can say to them, as Blake did:

> The vision of Christ which thou dost see
> Is my vision's chiefest enemy.
> Yours is the healer of mankind,
> Mine speaks in parables to the blind.

I see Jesus as a man whose perception of spiritual facts was extraordinarily intense. He was far more intelligent, as appears from his sayings, than his disciples. They misinterpreted his words, and as we only see him through their eyes we cannot know how he would appear to our own.

If Jesus were born in our time of a poor Jewish mother in capitalist Europe or North America he would receive a far wider education than 1900 years ago, when his reading was probably confined to the law and the prophets. Perhaps it was for this reason that his general ideas were always stated, either in parables drawn from everyday life, or in the terminology of religion. To-day he could talk in terms of science, psychology, and economics. So quite possibly we should not think of him primarily as a religious leader at all. In his own time he tried to simplify religion, and was accused of blasphemy. To-day most religious people would probably regard him as an infidel.

Most of us would first learn of his existence through

the Press. A reporter sent down to investigate a story of unprofessional cure of mental diseases writes a curious account of it. The healer is of an unusual type. So far from being sanctimonious, he is a confirmed beer-drinker. Indeed there is a story about that he miraculously put back all the pub clocks in Whitechapel at closing time. He has a keen sense of humour, and refuses to give a straight answer to religious queries. 'Come and live with me', he tells the reporter, 'if you want to find out about God.' 'I almost took him at his word', adds the reporter.

Later the police begin to take notice. This man is always talking about the coming revolution, sometimes in very violent terms. But it is difficult to pin him down. At one moment he says that he is an enemy of peace and has come to stir up disorder, at another that the revolution must take place in the mind. And his attitude to the rich is surprising in a revolutionary. He wants to abolish wealth, not because rich men are wicked, but because they are unhappy. 'It's easier for a motor lorry to get through a keyhole than for a rich man to enjoy life' he is reported to have said. The Communists hate him even more than the police and the parsons.

After two or three years he becomes an intolerable nuisance to the authorities. His followers have been making disturbances in churches and public places. The movement appears to be growing. Crucifixion is out of date. A trial offers too great an opportunity for publicity. A simple method is available for imprisoning an innocent man for life without trial. It is effectively used to-day by the Roman Catholic hierarchy in Canada against their opponents. The man has seen visions. A witness says that he stated that he was one with God.

Another asserts that he stated that he could rebuild the
law courts in three days. Two doctors, already jealous
of his unprofessional healing activities, certify him in-
sane. A devoted police agent who has actually managed
to become treasurer of the Man's movement smooths
the way for the arrest. His suicide shortly afterwards
merely proves that this maniac has spread insanity
around him, or so the Press affirms. Soon afterwards it
is announced that the madman has died in an asylum.
The plain man breathes a sigh of relief, and turns to the
financial column of the Press. He is one of the many
who, in the words of the Man, keep their heart in their
safe deposit.

But the affair is not over. Some of the Man's followers
say that he is still with them. Others are beginning to
spread his doctrines. They say that he has revolutionized psychology, and made it as practical as chemistry.
He has taught the art of happiness. You cannot love
yourself unless you love your neighbour first. If you
find fault with him it is a sign that you are really angry
with yourself. Some of these men and women disciples
certainly seem to exhibit a wholeness of personality
which is something fresh in the world. It often lands
them in prison, but an increasing section of the public
is attracted by their ideas, and still more by their manner
of life. The revolutionary idea is in the air that the rich
are a set of mutts who do not know how to enjoy life.
A few rich men and women actually give up their fortunes and claim to be tasting happiness for the first
time.

But another section of disciples have different ideas.
They stress the mystical side of their master's teaching
and his remarkable cures of disease. The authorities

encourage them. This will only be another new religion, and the State is not afraid of religions. In spite of occasional aberrations, religion makes for stable government.

The future is unknown. Has the Man started the real world revolution, or only another religion? The world's future depends on the answer.

THE GOLD-MAKERS

I AM more shameless than my colleagues about some things. I don't believe I know French better than most of them. But I don't mind talking it at a great rate without too meticulous a regard for genders. So every now and then I take a perfectly good holiday by giving a course of lectures in alleged French in Paris. Everyone is pleased by this arrangement. My university feels it is doing something for international co-operation, I manage to tell my French colleagues some things they don't know, and I learn any number of things I don't know myself. It's no good going to Germany, because the Germans read everything that is printed anywhere, and publish all they have done, and a bit more, at immense length. The French remain beautifully oblivious to a lot of work done outside France until everyone says French science is going to the dogs. Then it turns out that some perfectly obscure French man or woman has just discovered something really original and unlikely, such as radioactivity, or wave mechanics, which makes Einstein seem as simple as Rule of Three, and incidentally landed Eugène Galois in Devil's Island, and me (I sincerely hope) in the local gaol at Ambert.

I shouldn't have put in all this preface if I was publishing this narrative in the *Chemical Gazette* or the *British Journal of Physics*, as I originally thought of doing. But readers of this magazine might wonder what I was doing in the Rue Cujas at 11 P.M. on June 28, 1930, and why the man with no front teeth should have known who I am, and that I actually understand something about the application of wave mechanics to chemistry. The streets round the Sorbonne are placarded with lecture announcements, and my portrait had appeared in *L'Illustration* with a highly misleading biography. On the date in question I had just delivered my sixth and last lecture, and subsequently consumed a considerable quantity of very light beer with some French colleagues at the Café Soufflet, which is at the corner of the Boulevard St. Michel and the Rue des Écoles. I had sat there with my eminently respectable colleague Henriot and his wife, whilst one of his most brilliant pupils played backgammon at a neighbouring table with a little lady whose calling was not in doubt. I had reflected on the improbability of such a scene at Oxford or Cambridge, yet remembered a not utterly dissimilar occasion at the Cosmopolitan Club off Leith Walk in Edinburgh. But the Professor's wife had not been there.

The man with no front teeth was remarkably shabbily dressed, and looked hungry, which is unusual in Paris, where there is work for almost everybody to-day. He sidled up to me, and in a voice which was not rendered more intelligible by the absence of his teeth, said, 'For the love of Science read this, and if you want more, follow me'. He slunk on ahead of me and waited in the shadow of a doorway while I stood under a lamp and looked at the paper he had given me. It was the first part of the wave equation for carbon, or, rather, of the set of forty-two simultaneous differential equations which would enable one to predict the behaviour of that element if one could solve them. But it was expressed in a notation new to me, and certainly unpublished.

Now a beggar or a tout for some unsavoury concern
might conceivably have copied out some of Kultchagin's
equations to act as ground-bait for me, but he could not
possibly have transposed them like that. Imagine a man
handing you a copy of 'The Shropshire Lad' translated
faultlessly into Icelandic, and then written out in
Egyptian hieroglyphics, and you get an idea of the
intellectual effort involved and the special knowledge
needed. This was something really queer, and I am a
student of the really queer in physical chemistry, but
do not despise it when I meet it elsewhere. I followed
him. 'Bar du Progrès, Porte de la Villette, minuit', he
whispered. He was obviously in very considerable
terror, and motioned me to go on.

I had an hour before midnight. I felt that I might be
in for something odd, and after making sure that I was
not followed, I went into the Café d'Harcourt and over
a coffee wrote a note to my friend Bertaux, giving him
the facts and asking him to ring me up at my hotel at
noon next day, and to inform the police if I were missing. Then I boarded the Metro for the Porte de la
Villette, an exit from Paris which so far was only known
to me by its proximity on the map to the municipal
slaughterhouse. I was not as calm as I could have
wished, for as I entered the train I found that I had just
lit a threepenny cigar in oblivion of the fact that there
are no smoking compartments on the Metro, a fact
which I have always resented most keenly.

The Bar du Progrès is dim, but not really sinister. It
is extremely like some thousands of other bars. There is
the same fat lady behind the same zinc counter, the
same surprising variety of bottles behind her, the same
rather consumptive-looking waiter. At the back there is

T

a table in a recess, with two chairs. One occupant of the table can be seen from the door. The other is screened. I went in just before midnight, ordered a café cognac, and sat down facing the door. The only other customer was an inoffensive-looking lorry driver who was describing in considerable detail a collision in which he had, of course, been the innocent party, but which had detained him beyond his usual bed-time. On the stroke of midnight my friend of the Rue Cujas came in and without a word sat down in the seat opposite me. I ordered him another café cognac, and repeated the latter at suitable intervals during the next hour. I observed that the missing teeth were only one effect of what must have been a thoroughly nasty wound in the face. But the scars were old; it looked like a war wound. He spoke in a low voice for the best part of an hour in rapid and not easily intelligible French. Occasionally, at critical places in the story, he put in certain key words in English. Once or twice he made a scientific point in German. He was obviously suffering from extreme terror, but it was not the terror of the raw recruit during his first heavy shelling. It was the much grimmer emotion of the old soldier who realizes that there is a definite limit to human endurance, the terror of 1918. This is roughly what he told me. I don't think my recollection contains any serious errors on matters of fact.

'You have heard what happened to Eugène Galois?'

'I know he was found guilty of murder and sent to Devil's Island. But I can't believe he murdered a colleague for money. He's as big a mathematician as his namesake was a century ago. He might have committed a *crime passionnel*. Anyone with guts might do that. But you can't murder for gain unless your mind is obsessed by money, and his mind was too full of loxodromic groups to leave room for that sort of obsession. I hear they're trying to get his case retried. If I can do anything in reason to help, I will.'

'I'm glad you feel like that about Galois,' said my neighbour, 'but it's too late. He died last month of parrot disease. The convicts were allowed to keep pets, and there was an epidemic. He was a martyr. I am only talking to you because he is dead. He was on to the biggest thing since the invention of the steam-engine. He was murdered because he knew too much. If you listen to me, you may make world-history. You may quite possibly become the richest man on the planet. But you are also likely to be murdered. Indeed, if you have been seen with me you probably will be. But if you're afraid, you'd better clear out at once.'

I don't mind admitting that I was afraid. But since November 11, 1918, my adventures had been intellectual and emotional only. Moreover, I am ambitious. I fell a victim to my really lamentable propensity for quotation, and reminded myself,

He either fears his fate too much, or his deserts are small,
Who dares not put it to the touch, to gain or lose it all.

'Go on,' I said. I also repeated under my breath a line from a less reputable poem, which I had found consolatory on unpleasant occasions during the war, to the effect that, whatever happened, I should be 'damnable mouldy a hundred years hence'. He went on.

'Galois was a man of genius. You know that. But you don't perhaps realize how broad his interests were. He felt very deeply that the evils of the present day were

due to the application of science by unscientific men.
"We have given humanity a large degree of control over
matter, and they have given us modern war and modern
industry", he used to say. So he determined to apply
his science according to his own ideas, not those of
financiers. He had a special down on financiers. He
realized that wave mechanics meant a new era in chemistry. When he heard that Eucken and Bonhöfer had
proved hydrogen to be a mixture he said it was only
the beginning. He had some private means, and after his
last published paper he went off to the country, and
worked out the wave equations for the gold atom. You
will realize the stupendous nature of that. A man with
the mathematical ability to do it could have determined
the orbit of the new planet Pluto in one evening in a
café with the band playing. He bought a cottage in the
country and had the walls papered white. He went
round the different rooms with a step-ladder, covering
the paper with calculations. Of course he filled masses
of note-books too. But he said he needed the walls for
the main results, and by writing them up in that way he
knew how to find what he wanted. He worked eight
hours a day for a year and a half, and at the end of that
time he had his principal results in a single note-book.
I have seen it, but you will soon hear why I haven't got
it. In another half-year he had worked out that gold
must have an enormous and quite unsuspected affinity
for a certain group of organic compounds. Then he got
hold of Riquier, an organic chemist who had been with
him at the École Normale, and Riquier made one of the
compounds in question. They showed that their scheme
would work on a laboratory scale. Then they approached
me.

'My name is Martin. That is irrelevant. I do not
think that I shall live long. I was a works chemist at
Nanterre and a friend of Riquier's. We went down together to Ste. Leocadie, a little village on the sea coast,
in Bouches du Rhône, near Aigues Mortes, where there
is a large lagoon. We started a salt-pan. I don't know
that the salt was particularly good, but we managed to
sell it, anyway. That, however, wasn't what we were
after. You know there is gold in sea water. Not very
much, about one part in twenty million. When you
evaporate the water in a salt-pan, most of the salt
crystallizes out, and you are left with a sticky solution
full of Epsom salts and what not. Almost all the gold is
in there, so it is easy to concentrate it a hundred times
in the sunlight of southern France. You can crystallize
out most of the rest of the salts without losing much
gold. The brine left behind has about one part in
200,000 of gold. That's a lot. Gravel with only one part
in a million has been worked profitably, and even on the
Rand the quartz only averages twelve parts in a million
of gold. You take your residual solution and add about
eight parts in a million of Riquier's compound, which
we called auron. I don't know what it is, but it is bright
blue, and it is made from a saponine, and I believe has two
pyrrole rings in its molecule. You leave the mixture for
an hour, and then bubble air through it. The blue stuff
has combined with the gold to make a red compound.
This is a surface active substance, and it all comes into
the froth which you blow off the top. You dry the froth,
add a little acid, and out comes the gold. You can use
the blue stuff again, but we used to lose about 5 per
cent. at each operation.

'My job was to run the bubbling tanks. Riquier made

the stuff, and Galois saw to sales and purchases. There were some local men, chosen for their stupidity, who looked after the salt-pans, and I acted as foreman there. We started in January 1929, but it wasn't till May that we got the process working perfectly, and from May to September we got out about four million francs' worth of gold, £30,000, or a little more. Most of that went in paying off our debts, but we had a million or so of clear profit. Of course before the show started we had decided what to do with the money. We were all somewhat idealistic. You have to be idealistic to go in for science in France to-day, when a professor gets £300 a year or so as the reward of a distinguished career. Our immediate idea was to go straight ahead until we had a thousand million francs, and then to start endowing science as it ought to be endowed, so that a good scientific worker was paid as well as a good engineer or surgeon, and a reasonable amount was available for apparatus. Naturally, we thought most of France, Belgium, and Italy, where scientific workers are worst paid. But we hadn't forgotten Germany, and we had a few schemes even for England and America. Well, that's all over! If you succeed where we failed, don't forget French science.'

'I'm not likely to,' I said.

'We reckoned to make some hundred millions of francs without exciting much notice, but obviously the thing couldn't go on indefinitely. But here Galois had his plans. He believed that the world was not producing gold quickly enough. If humanity increases its stock of gold more slowly than its other material wealth, prices will fall and you will get unemployment. That is what is happening now. If we made gold too quickly, say thirty thousand million francs a year, prices would rise, and all the world would be like France and Germany after the war. Galois's idea was to produce gold just fast enough to keep prices steady on an average. "The thing will be too big for any one man," said Galois, "and if I gave it to the French Government the country would be flooded with gold, and our agriculture and manufactures would die like those of Spain did after the conquest of Mexico and Peru. No, we'll give France enough to pay her foreign debts, but the secret, and the control of the thing, must go to the League of Nations, and the day they get it America and the Soviets will join up."

'Well, everything went swimmingly till the end of last August. Then I got a typewritten document from Paris. There was no address, but it was headed Association Internationale pour la Défense des Interêts Rentiers. It ran roughly like this:

'DEAR SIR—As it is possible that in future the operations on which you are engaged will incommode us, I have the honour to offer you an income of two hundred thousand francs per year should you abandon them. Your colleagues have also been approached. In the event of your resigning your occupation, you will receive your first quarter's salary within one week, the notes being despatched to your mother's house. In earnest of our good intentions we enclose 10,000 francs.

'Should the offer not be accepted within one week from to-day, we shall be compelled to take steps to eliminate the concern in which you are a partner.

'A.I.D.I.R.

'I was impressed by the ten thousand francs, but still more by the fact that when I looked at the letter three days later the paper had crumbled to powder. As a chemist I can imagine how this might be done, but it would take some working out. For that showed that our enemies had skill and knowledge behind them, as well as money. The fact that they had destroyed this evidence meant that there was probably something in their threats.

'I talked it over with my colleagues. They had had similar letters. Unfortunately they were against warning the police, as they didn't want to give away what we were doing. Galois thought the A.I.D.I.R. might be what it purported to be, a representative of a financial group interested in fixed-interest-bearing securities, which would of course fall in value if we flooded the world with gold, while ordinary shares and equities would rise. Riquier and I, rightly as it turned out, believed that they really stood for a gold-mining group.

'I never found out how they discovered our secret. Galois and I used to take our gold by car to a bank at Cette. Someone connected with that may have got suspicious and tracked us. Possibly Riquier may have talked too much to a lady who I think was his mistress. But I doubt it.

'Next week I was rung up on the telephone. The voice said, "A.I.D.I.R. speaking. Our offer is and remains open. We are even prepared to raise it if you state your terms in the advertisement column of the *Petit Nîmois*. If you do not accept, you will all be killed. This is our last communication."

'I found later that the call had been made at a public call office in Nîmes. We agreed to take no notice, but started a scheme of defences. We all had automatic pistols, and Riquier made us a supply of lachrymatory gas bombs. The factory was easily defensible, and we had burglar alarms, and a couple of fairly excitable dogs.

The other two were enthusiasts, and I am not much afraid of death. As you see, my face got fairly smashed up in the war.'

He lifted his rather long and dirty hair, and I noticed that, besides the damage to his mouth, he had no left ear.

'At that time I had some false teeth, which I have just pawned in order to live. But I have been in constant pain since 1916, so I do not find life immensely attractive, even when I am not being hunted.

'Towards the end of September I developed a boil on my neck, and had to go into a clinic for two days to have it lanced. While I was away, the blow fell. Riquier was found shot outside the factory door. Two Swiss tourists swore that they had seen Galois shoot him after a quarrel. The bullets fitted a pistol which a Marseilles gunsmith swore Galois had bought from him, and which was found near the body. Several other witnesses turned up later, and swore to the most incredible lies, which hung together to make a pretty damning story. Almost simultaneously an alleged Chilian millionaire called Fernandez sued Galois for six million francs which he claimed to have lent him for a scheme for extracting gold from sea water. Apparently he had a large outfit of forged documents. As you know, the jury found that Galois was a swindler and a murderer. I got hold of his lawyer, and offered to give evidence, but he thought it would be useless, and I lay low. But the A.I.D.I.R. people found me. As I was coming home one night I was attacked by three men. I didn't want to shoot and get jailed, as I probably would have been. I managed to burst a lachrymatory bomb among them, and left them weeping. But I have been on the run ever since. Meanwhile Fernandez was able to seize the factory for debt,

and presumably got our documents and about a kilo-
gram of auron.

'Even after his condemnation Galois's lawyer believed
in him. He found out some odd facts. He established
that both Fernandez and one of the supposed Swiss
were connected with the same gold-mining group.'

That was the end of our conversation, because at this
point I noticed a bomb coming towards me through the
air. Up till that moment I had refused to decide between
two alternatives—that M. Martin's story was true, or
that he was a very good liar. I had a strong suspicion
that he would shortly ask me to lend him a hundred
francs. I felt that I had had my money's worth, and
proposed to lend him a hundred and fifty, for good
lying is a rare gift which should be encouraged.

The bomb, however, convinced me that he had been
speaking the truth. But its immediate effect was to jerk
me back for thirteen years into the past. It was very unfortunate indeed for the throwers of this bomb that
hand grenades had been my special line during the
Great War. I am one of the few people who ran a bombing school for nine months without casualties. Among
the things which we occasionally did as demonstrations
was to catch lighted bombs and throw them back, or
more accurately, sideways, out of the trench. I had a
one-eyed and rarely quite sober corporal who used to
do this, but I sometimes did it myself. I admit that we
used to lengthen the time-fuse beforehand. Provided
you are a good judge of time, it is no more dangerous
than crossing the road among motor traffic, but it is
more impressive to onlookers. Some idiot asked questions about it in Parliament, and got an Army Order
issued forbidding the practice.

This bomb was a 'stick bomb' with a long wooden handle. I think it was a German type with a five-seconds time fuse. Looking past the bomb through the door of the café, I saw two men in a car, one at the wheel, and one who had clearly just thrown it. The car was moving slowly. I reckoned that the charge would explode in another three seconds. As the bomb, which was thrown with a very good aim, landed in my coffee-cup, I caught it by the handle, and ran towards the door, swinging it as I did so. The man standing in the car was expecting me to run out, so he fired at me. But he was not expecting me to return the bomb, so he fired very erratically. One bullet went through my raincoat. Another, as I afterwards learnt, hit the lady behind the counter, but not fatally. As I reached the door, I pitched the bomb neatly into the car, which was now accelerating, and threw myself flat on my face with more speed than elegance, as I had been accustomed to do when a machine-gun opened fire on me.

The bomb burst as I reached the ground. The man with the revolver was jumping from the car as it did so. A piece wounded him, and he fell on the pavement. The driver could not escape, and the explosion lifted him into the air. His body, oddly twisted, fell back into the car as it struck a lamp-post and burst into flames. I got up and ran past the blazing car. As I passed the man on the pavement, I kicked his head as hard as I could. Some bone in it broke with a crack. I ran my fastest down a side street, dodged round several corners, and was violently sick. The burning car lit up the sky behind me as I walked with deliberate slowness on to the Rue de Flandres. I saw no sign of Martin, and nobody followed me. I was fortunate enough to catch, within a very few minutes, an omnibus going to the Châtelet, one of those which run at hourly intervals throughout the night. I got off just before the terminus, and walked to my hotel by a round-about route.

I am fairly sure that I was not followed, for on several occasions I turned corners when no one was in sight. I reflected for a short time on my adventures, and on the fact that I had not paid for the coffee. I regretted this, for I am rather scrupulous in small matters. I also hoped that I had killed the man on the pavement, or at least given him severe enough concussion to blot out his memory of recent events. In that case there would probably be no one who had seen me with Martin, and I stood a chance of becoming the modern equivalent of Midas. Meanwhile, however, there was nothing to be done, and rather unexpectedly I fell asleep within half an hour of getting to bed.

I did not wake up next morning until about ten. I came to the conclusion that I had better clear out for England at once. As soon as I had dressed I telephoned to Bertaux that I was all right, but had to leave Paris. I told him to keep his mouth shut, and to lunch with me at one o'clock. I then took a bus to my bank in the Place de la Concorde, and drew out two thousand francs for my hotel bill and railway ticket. There had been no account of last night's little affair in the morning paper, but when I left the bank I bought a *Paris-Midi*, which devoted a column to the outrage of the Bar du Progrès. The man in the car was dead, although a baker had burned his hands badly in an attempt to rescue him. Another man, presumably the one with the revolver, was in hospital with a wound in the shoulder and a fractured jaw. So was the proprietress. The waiter had seen me throwing a bomb, but apparently no one had seen the bomb coming in! Fortunately he gave a very vague description of me, and had overheard Martin and me talking in German, but not in English. He also said that I spoke French with a German accent, in which he was not so far out. Being a Scotsman, I do not talk it with an English accent. If I go into a café full of young ladies eager to make my acquaintance, it is often simplest to keep off the rest by standing one of them a drink. In such a case I always ask her to guess my nationality. She then suggests Dutch, Danish, Polish, and Czecho-Slovak. I assume that I am really taken for a German, but that the young lady, being too polite to make such a suggestion, names the various neighbouring States.

I went to the Gare du Nord for a ticket, and for a reservation on the four o'clock train. As I left the station I noticed a man with a black moustache in a bowler hat looking at me rather intently. I got into a taxi and ordered the driver to go to the restaurant where Bertaux was expecting me. I gave the directions in a fairly low voice, so I hardly think the watcher could have overheard me. He got into another taxi, and I noticed it following us. I did not wish to involve Bertaux in my little troubles. I also wanted to be perfectly sure that I was being fol-lowed, and, if possible, to shake the man off. So instead of going to my restaurant near the Sorbonne, I told the driver to go the the Gare du Luxembourg.

I can just remember the time when the London Metropolitan was worked by steam-engines. Those of my readers who regret those romantic days are advised to travel by the Chemin de Fer de Sceaux et Limours, a suburban railway line which starts from the Gare du Luxembourg and leaves Paris by an extremely long

tunnel which is always full of a particularly suffocating
smoke. I bought a ticket for Massy-Verrières, an undistinguished station on that undistinguished line. My
pursuer followed me. I went down and got into the
fullest compartment I could find. He got in close behind
me. At the first stop, the Gare de Port Royal, still in
Paris, I dashed out through the smoke and up the stairs.
My unknown friend followed. But here I had a stroke of
luck. Just outside the station there was one—and only
one—taxi. I boarded it and told the man to go to the
Institut Pasteur. I crouched to offer as small a target as
possible if my unknown friend opened fire. Fortunately
he did not. As we turned the first corner I looked back
and saw him running after me. I do not know when he
finally lost sight of me, but, as I went down to the Metro
station in the Boulevard Pasteur, to which I had diverted
my vehicle, I saw a taxi driving up at a rather dangerous
speed. Four different lines, however, leave that station,
and if he was still chasing me, he must have taken the
wrong train.

After several changes on the Metro, I arrived rather
late at my restaurant. Bertaux was waiting, but had
nearly finished lunch. I told him I was being followed
by would-be murderers, and was going to run for it. As
I refused to take his advice and go to the police I think
that he suspected my pursuer of being an irate husband.
That is the worst of these romantics. I had no intention
of going back to my hotel, for if my identity was known
it might be watched. I asked Bertaux to go for a small
suitcase which I had already packed with my more
essential clothes and shaving things. He was to say I
would call round for my trunk later. I had just finished
lunch when he came back. I determined to run in the

opposite direction from England, in the hope that my
enemies were only watching the west-bound trains, so I
went straight to the Gare de l'Est and bought a ticket
for Berne, hoping to work round from there to one of
the German air ports and fly home.

Even as I bought my ticket I noticed, or seemed to
notice, a man who looked at me closely and then went
to a telephone box. I did not see him again after this,
and my journey was uneventful as far as Belfort. But in
the *Soir*, which I had bought, I found two interesting
items. The man with the broken jaw had given his name.
It was presumably false, but this meant that he could
speak. On the same page was a not uncommon headline,
'Un Inconnu se suicide'—'Suicide of Unknown Man'.
The man in question, who had been found hanged from
the scaffolding of a suburban cinema under construction,
had no left ear, and his front teeth were missing. Nothing
was found on his person but a crude scrawl stating that
he was fed up. So they had got Martin. Possibly they
had forced my name out of him before his murder. In
any case, I proposed to do my best to escape his fate.

It was night when I got to Belfort. As the train ran
into the station I saw on the platform my friend who
had chased me earlier in the day, with two other men.
Presumably he at least had flown to Belfort.

I may well have done him an injustice, but the events
of the past twenty hours had somewhat prejudiced me
against him, and, although I was not certain whether he
intended to murder me or merely to hand me over to
the police on a charge of bombing his friends, I did not
feel called upon to put his intentions to an experimental
test. I am sure he had not seen me when I rapidly left
the compartment, and before the train had drawn up,

bolted myself into a lavatory, where I remained. I had taken my handbag, as there was still a chance that my name was not known to my hunters.

Five minutes after leaving Belfort I had some luck. If I had not, I should not be alive and writing this account. The train drew up, as I had hoped it would, and clearly not in a station, as there were no lights. I dashed out of my retreat, opened a door, and jumped out of the train on the left-hand side. As I did so, the train began to move. Someone fired two or three shots at me. Presumably they missed because the train was moving and I was already fifteen yards away. Then a train going towards Paris, for which we had no doubt been waiting, cut in between me and the gunman. I did not stop running, and soon reached a road, where my luck still held. A lorry was waiting at a level crossing for the trains to pass. I asked for, and got, a lift. It appeared that the lorry was going from Strasbourg to Lons-le-Saunier with the household effects of a sub-prefect. For a hundred francs the driver was willing to take me to Besançon, where he was stopping for the night. I suspected that I might be chased, so I took him into my confidence, or, more accurately, half-way in. Having received a sound classical education, I remembered Odysseus, and the advantage of economy of truth when in tight corners. I judged the driver to be romantic in the worst sense of the word. Sailors, it is said, have a wife in every port, but ports are confined to sea coasts and large rivers and canals, whereas lorries can visit any town in a civilized country. Lorry drivers of a polygamous disposition are thus peculiarly favoured by their professional duties.

I therefore informed him that I had formed a romantic

attachment for the *poule* of a millionaire, and persuaded her to flee to Switzerland. The irate lover had pursued me while I was attempting to join her, and had tried to have me murdered in the train. As it was likely that he, or one of his myrmidons, would chase me in a car, I desired to hide among the furniture of the sub-prefect. Another fifty francs secured me a place on the top of a bale of carpets under a table, the tarpaulin was drawn over me, and we started off. I had sufficient experience of lorry-jumping in the Great War to guess that I had not chosen a bed of roses. And this was a particularly ancient lorry. By bracing my arms and legs against the table-top I managed on the whole to avoid hitting the under side of the table when the lorry kicked its tail into the air, but the strain was considerable, and I was already aching, and had hit the table once, when, after ten minutes, the lorry stopped with a jarring of the brakes and an explosion of language.

The French tongue is peculiarly ill-adapted for abuse. Theological invective is useless among a nation who are now mostly rationalists, and even in their religious days had a sneaking regard for the Devil. And anatomical and physiological terms which horrify the Anglo-Saxon do not shock the Latin. So the special vocabulary of abuse is largely confined to the monosyllable which Marshal Cambronne used at Waterloo. This word circulated freely while my saviour denied having seen me, much less given me a lift. He even applied it to an offer of fifty francs to look under the tarpaulin. He also mentioned the police. I heard the voices of two other men in discussion, and drew out my only weapon, a large penknife, not so much in the hope of saving my life, as on the principle enunciated by Macbeth, that,

U

'Whiles I see lives, the gashes do better upon them'. I am a Scotsman, like Macbeth. I proposed to close with one of my assailants and aim at his jugular vein, for the bullets from a small-bore automatic pistol, though quite efficient killers, have little immediate stopping power. The discussion continued, the details being inaudible. Finally my saviour produced his last verbal card. 'Tristes individus', he began a sentence, but before he had finished it I heard the noise of a large car accelerating. They had thought better of it. After all, one cannot hold up all the recalcitrant lorry drivers of a Department at the pistol's point.

At this moment I made the bravest decision of my life. I refused an offer to come out from my hiding-place. The next two hours were the most unpleasant I have ever passed, and I have been through three intense bombardments and had one septic wound. When we arrived at Besançon I was bruised all over, and bleeding in a number of places. As the lorry driver stood me a stiff cognac for which he insisted on paying, he informed me that the men in the car had passed him again on their way back to Belfort, and looked at him closely. So at least I had saved my life.

I was extremely tired as well as sore, but I lost no time about my next step. With their clearly efficient organization I assumed that the A.I.D.I.R. would discover my identity in a day or so, if they did not know it already. I wrote to a friend in London (for obvious reasons I do not mention his name) to say that I desired the story to appear in the Press that I had disappeared suddenly from Paris, leaving my luggage behind. I also wrote a letter dated from Munich to my cousin Polly, better known as Meg o' Mayfair, the lady who meets a duchess a day in the gossip columns of the *Daily Excess*. I told her that I was feeling very run down after my lectures, and had been so absent-minded as to leave most of my luggage in Paris. I was going off for a walking tour in the Böhmer Wald, and hoped to see her when I returned in a month or two. I did not feel that Polly would be able to avoid contributing the gist of this note to the news columns. Another letter from the same address to my Parisian landlady stated that I would return to call for my luggage and pay my bill, although I guessed that the A.I.D.I.R. would probably do both on my behalf. I enclosed these letters to a friend who was working at the Bavarian Academy of Sciences, with an urgent request to post them, burn the covering letter, and keep his mouth shut.

I reckoned that although the A.I.D.I.R. would probably not take this too seriously, they would be bound to divert a little energy to Germany, and if they failed to find me within a fortnight or so, they might begin to transfer their energies across the frontier. Meanwhile I slept, although it was clear from the state of the sheets that the spot on which I laid my head had supported many boots in the past.

In the grey dawn my chauffeur woke me. I suppressed a desire to see Goya's 'Scenes of Cannibalism' in the local picture gallery, though this would have accorded well with my mood, and continued my journey. I again refused to sit outside, but this time I was packed more scientifically and rattled rather little. By request the lorry halted on a deserted part of the road near Poligny, about thirty miles on. I kept up my romance, and said that I proposed to walk to the Swiss frontier, and cross by the Col de St. Georges, a good day's walk up through the Jura. But my plans were different. I walked in the opposite direction, making for the centre of France by unfrequented roads.

As I walked I tried to consider my situation as a purely intellectual problem. The A.I.D.I.R. probably believe that Martin knew how to make auron, and has told me the secret. But in any case I know enough to make it worth their while to murder me. If the bomb had been thrown five minutes later I should be in a better position to judge whether they intend to flood the world with gold, or merely to suppress the secret and guard their profits. I suspect the latter, for they would not be likely to keep the secret for long. While they believe that by murdering me they can hush the thing up, they will try to do so. I am therefore taking what I think to be the safest, though not the noblest course. I am publishing all I know on the subject of gold extraction from sea-water. Until publication they will try to murder me. But I hope that my account will appear simultaneously in England and the United States in magazines which generally contain fiction. Many of their readers may suppose this story to be fiction. But if I am murdered, or imprisoned on a false charge, like Galois, this will constitute an advertisement to the whole world that I have written the truth.

Even the A.I.D.I.R. cannot comb out the whole of France for me, though they may possibly put the French police on my track. But they are doubtless watching the French frontiers, the British ports, and my university. They may even contrive to open letters to my friends, but they will hardly suspect me of publishing the most practically important discovery of the century in popular magazines. I am writing this manuscript in a little walled town in Auvergne, where I arrived a week after the rather hectic day which I have here chronicled. On the way I have done my best to sink my identity. I have removed all names and marks from my clothes, burnt my passport, and exchanged my suitcase for a knapsack. I have even gone so far as to remove the buttons from my clothes, and substitute French buttons. Sewing is not one of my accomplishments, and not only did I prick my fingers, but several of my buttons are insecure. My beard is growing nicely. In fact I think of wearing one permanently in future. Also, I got ten francs for my razor. In Clermont-Ferrand I bought a French-Danish dictionary. As soon as the manuscript is accepted for publication, I am asking the firm who will act as my agents to put an advertisement in the *Petit Parisien* on three consecutive days, giving the date when the news will be published. The advertisement will be a request to the creditors of a mythical American lately deceased, to write to a lawyer (also I hope mythical) in Baltimore, before a certain date. I, and I alone, shall know that that date is the date of publication, and until then I must conceal my identity. I shall wander about France as long as my money lasts, and even try to earn a little more. I got five francs yesterday for assisting a motorist, whose engine had broken down, to carry a suitcase to the nearest village. I dare not write to England for money, as this would give my address away if letters to my acquaintances are opened. Also it might be difficult to get a letter without producing evidence of my identity.

I am living as cheaply as I can, but my expenses are much increased by the law of the land. In England anyone may sleep in the open, provided he has a shilling on his person to rebut the charge of being without visible means of support. But in France, to quote Anatole France from memory, 'The law with majestic impartiality forbids the rich, no less than the poor, to sleep in ditches or under haystacks'. That is the worst of Equality. Unless I can get a job, my money will run out in a month at most. Shortly before it is all spent, I propose to seek the shelter of the only available free lodging, namely prison. I may, of course, be run in anywhere for having no identity papers, but my plan is to go to Ambert, get rather drunk, and be arrested. I shall then say that I am a native of Iceland, and have lost my passport. The local Danish vice-consul will presumably appear. I worked for three months in Copenhagen at the Institute of Theoretical Physics, and know enough Danish to be fairly rude, and a smattering of the modern Icelandic dialect. Besides, I am spending two hours a day with my dictionary. So I am going to be Mr. Thorgrim Magnusson, an ardent Icelandic home-ruler, who objects to all Danish officials as representatives of a foreign domination. I hope that I shall be so unpleasant that the Danes will refuse to accept me, and the French will keep me in jail. I do not particularly relish the idea of hard labour in a French prison, but it is preferable to the fate of Galois, Riquier, and Martin. Also I have a theory, which I devoutly hope is correct, that prisoners are allowed to smoke in France.

The moment my story is published, I appeal to my friends and relations to take all possible steps to get me released. I shall also give my real name. But if no prisoner of the name of Thorgrim Magnusson is to be found in the jails of Auvergne, it may be presumed that I have met the fate of Martin. Only yesterday I saw an individual who appeared to be following me. I went up the nearest hill and outdistanced him. But I cannot believe that the A.I.D.I.R. have agents everywhere, and I suspect he was merely struck by my rather unkempt appearance. I believe that I shall get away with it.

What will happen after this story is published I do not know. I do not propose to emulate Galois and shall not try to make gold. I will not even take holidays at the seaside. Obviously if I knew the formula for auron and intended to work the process, I should not have given away half the secret. I shall certainly be watched, but I credit the A.I.D.I.R. with sufficient intelligence not to assassinate me. They will hope that this story will be taken as the ingenious attempt of a professor to explain his otherwise discreditable arrest for drunkenness. I take it, however, that someone will have the wits to see that it is a perfectly true story, and that Galois' process will be working somewhere within the next ten years. I hope so, because I should like to see the men who organized the murder of Galois and his friends picking crusts out of the gutter. A team of fairly good mathematicians could do the requisite calculations in four years or so. So about six years hence I recommend my readers to sell out shares in gold-mines and fixed-interest-bearing securities, and to buy industrials. But there are some very good mathematical physicists in Russia, and if the Bolsheviks get hold of the process first there will be about £1,000,000,000 per year available for the purposes of the world revolution. In that case the purchase of securities of any kind will be pointless.

By WYNDHAM LEWIS

PALEFACE. The Philosophy of the 'Melting-Pot.' "Strong, brilliant, splendid stuff it is."—*The Times.* Cr. 8vo, 7s. 6d.

TIME AND WESTERN MAN. "He has attempted the first serious reply to Bergson and the mathematical philosophers that I have seen in English. Thought can only be countered by thought, and here, radiant with life, is first-rate thinking."—*Humbert Wolfe* in *The Observer.* Demy 8vo, 21s.

By C. E. MONTAGUE

A WRITER'S NOTES ON HIS TRADE. "It is a very good book."—*Arnold Bennett* in *The Evening Standard. IInd Printing.* Cr. 8vo, 7s. 6d.

DISENCHANTMENT. "In describing the progress of a human soul through the purgatory of the war to the disillusion of the peace, Mr. Montague has written a very fine book. . . . I have seen no book about the war so temperate and so human."— *John Masefield.* Cr. 8vo, 7s. vIth *Printing.* Phoenix Library, 3s. 6d.

By ALDOUS HUXLEY

JESTING PILATE. The Diary of a Journey through India, Burma, Japan, the United States, etc. "It is never dull, and we pass with engaging rapidity from scene to scene."—*Sir Edmund Gosse* in *The Sunday Times.* Illustrated. Ivth *Printing.* Cr. 8vo, 7s. 6d. Phoenix Library, 3s. 6d.

PROPER STUDIES. Sociological and other essays. "His book is a vital contribution to modern thought."—*Illustrated London News. IInd Printing.* Phoenix Library, 3s. 6d.

By ALDOUS HUXLEY—*continued*

DO WHAT YOU WILL. Essays. "The book of a man whose knowledge and activity of mind is that of a leader of his generation."—*Frank Swinnerton* in *The Evening News.* II*nd Printing.* Cr. 8vo, 7s. 6d.

ALONG THE ROAD. "*Notes and Essays of a Tourist.*" "No wonder that Mr. Huxley's reputation is high when he writes so well."—*Times Literary Supplement.* Narrow Cr. 8vo, 7s. 6d. v*th Printing.* Phoenix Library, 3s. 6d.

By JULIAN HUXLEY

ESSAYS IN POPULAR SCIENCE. "He has inherited a remarkable gift for lucid and entertaining exposition."—*Saturday Review.* Illustrated. Cr. 8vo, 7s. 6d. II*nd Printing.* Phoenix Library, 3s. 6d.

ESSAYS OF A BIOLOGIST. "A brilliant book of serious purpose and with a happy style; and it is by a maker of new biological knowledge who is also a scholar and a poet."—*Professor J. Arthur Thompson.* Cr. 8vo, 7s. 6d. v*th Printing.* Phoenix Library, 3s. 6d.

By J. B. S. HALDANE

POSSIBLE WORLDS. Scientific Essays. "These essays will provide almost any intelligent reader with effective mental stimuli such as few books afford." —*The Nation.* Cr. 8vo, 7s. 6d. v*th Printing.* Phoenix Library, 3s. 6d.

By ROGER FRY

TRANSFORMATIONS. "Mr. Fry's contributions to æsthetics are always interesting as the product of a fine intelligence brought to bear on a wealth of genuine æsthetic experience."—*Monthly Criterion.* Illustrated. Demy 4to, 31s. 6d.

VISION AND DESIGN. Essays on Art. "Mr. Fry is an authority to be respected. It is ours to learn where he has much to teach."—*Liverpool Courier.* v*th Printing.* Phoenix Library, 3s. 6d.